CHOSEN AS A 2021
BY *THE*.

'Hawari's distinctive, laconi   ɟ ——ᴘ…
horror of settler-colonialism and the lengths families go to
[to] survive.'
— *The New Arab*

'In narrativising, "legitimacy" is not only brutally bureau-
cratic but also informed and defined by hegemonic power.
The Stone House resituates Palestinian orators within their
authority to archive—and analyse—historical events,
explicitly citing lived experience and collective past as
examples of credible material evidence. Unconcerned
with traditionally ethnocentric and effacing storytelling
standards, this book asserts that the Nakba is best told
by those with the bruises, not those with the batons. Yara
Hawari establishes a historical portrait that gives life to the
nuances of settler colonialism that are frequently kept out
of the headlines.'
— Mohammed El-Kurd, author of *Rifqa*

'A rigorous, feminist engagement with the history of the
Palestinian tragedy. Through the stories of one family
from the Galilee, Hawari explores the multifarious experiences of exile, displacement, survival and return.'
— Isabella Hammad, author of *The Parisian*

'A powerful story told with great care for humans' capacity
to remember and resist. Through memory and oral history,

THE STONE HOUSE

First published in the United Kingdom in 2021
by Hajar Press C.I.C.
www.hajarpress.com
@hajarpress

ISBN 978-1-914221-04-0 Paperback
ISBN 978-1-914221-10-1 EPUB eBook

A Cataloguing-in-Publication data record for this book is
available from the British Library.

Cover and interior art: Hanna Stephens
Cover design: Samara Jundi
Map: Dana Abu Asab, Zeindee Designs
Typesetting: Laura Jones / lauraflojo.com

Printed and bound in the United Kingdom by
Clays Ltd, Elcograf S.p.A.

THE STONE HOUSE

YARA HAWARI

For the descendants of Hamda.

One day the stone house will be returned to us.

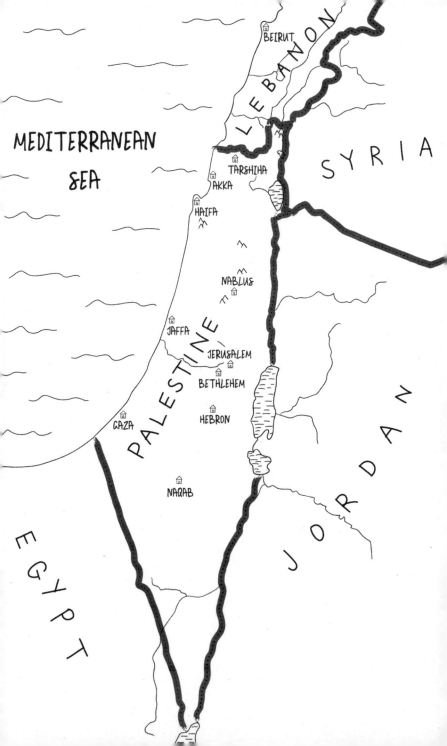

AUTHOR'S NOTE

Like many indigenous communities, for Palestinians, oral history is one of our most crucial tools against erasure. Storytelling, al-hakawati, is an ingrained cultural practice, but it can also be a steadfast form of resistance against a dominant historical narrative that seeks to eliminate all other narratives. This book hopes to make a small contribution to this resistance, in particular through recording a part of Palestinian history that is often forgotten: the stories of the Palestinian community within the 1948 territories and their survival amidst the ashes of the Nakba.

This book is also a deeply personal endeavour—indeed, the three main characters are my father, grandmother and great-grandmother. Their memories are also those of our people and were instilled in me from a young age; I absorbed them readily and eagerly until they became intertwined with my own. It was in this ephemeral cognitive realm of inherited stories, personal and collective, that I sought solace and temporary relief from the world around me. I was able to bring the destroyed Palestinian landscape to life and simultaneously blur out the colonisers' infrastructure. I could revive long-lost relatives and imagine our community whole, intact and unfragmented. And I was able to breathe.

It is my great regret that I did not speak more to my grandmother and great-grandmother about the events and intricacies of their daily lives. Yet, there is so much repetition across Palestinian history that their feelings and experiences are not hard to imagine. Much of this book was written during the Unity Intifada, which was sparked by resistance against expulsions in the Palestinian neighbourhood of Sheikh Jarrah in Jerusalem. As I was putting pen to paper to archive my great-grandmother's struggle to stay in her home over six decades ago, another generation of Palestinians was rising up against displacement and dispossession today.

PLAYLIST

Firqat al-'Ashiqin – 'Min Sijn 'Akka'

Fairuz – 'Le Beirut'

The Beatles – 'Sgt. Pepper's Lonely Hearts Club Band'

Pink Floyd – 'Another Brick in the Wall'

Souad Massi – 'Raoui'

Sanaa Moussa – 'Wea'youneha'

Faraj Suleiman – 'Questions on My Mind'

Bu Kolthoum – 'Zamilou'

Daboor & Shabjdeed (Prod. Al Nather) – 'Inn Ann'

Shab Abed – 'Atab (Hadi Zeidan Remake)'

MAHMOUD

Mahmoud climbed the stairs of the bus and made his way towards the back. He had arrived early to reserve his place in the back row before his classmates. Everyone knew that those who sat in the back row commanded authority over the rest of the children. Once claimed, the seat would be his for the rest of the long trip from his village in the country's north to the newly occupied territories. Mahmoud crammed his bag under the seat in front and sat down. Glancing out of the window, he searched for his mother amidst the throng of parents. He spotted her immediately. She stood out from the other fallah women with her typical Bedouin features—curly hair, dark eyes and striking jawline—so distinctive that people called her 'Dheeba al-Badawiya'. Her hair was neatly parted at the side, with a loose scarf resting on her shoulders. Her floral dress fell just below her knees. She liked to dress up fashionably for special occasions—something she considered today to be. Mahmoud's father often teased her that it was a habit she had picked up in Beirut.

As Mahmoud locked eyes with her, the anxious lines on his mother's face eased. She had been worried about the trip, and Mahmoud knew she didn't want him to go. He had spent hours reassuring her that it was safe and that the war was over. In fact, rather humiliatingly, the war had lasted less than a week. The Zionists had seized and occupied more territory following the crushing defeat of the Arab armies. Both sides of what the world was calling the 'Green Line' had been reunited. But it wasn't the reunification that Mahmoud had hoped for. The Israeli state now had full control over not only what was once historic Palestine, but also the Egyptian Sinai and the Syrian Golan. It was being hailed as a remarkable victory. 'A young state, against all odds,' reported foreign news stations. Mahmoud thought this unfair, considering that the state in question was backed by the world's strongest imperial powers. Worse yet, there was a story that deliberately wasn't being told. It was as if Palestine had never existed and this state always had—a phenomenal feat of rewriting history. While the new state's power and consolidation of territory seemed irreversible, Mahmoud's mother was still worried about an impending war—that they would close the borders all of a sudden, leaving Mahmoud stuck on the other side. It was unlikely, but Dheeba's fear wasn't completely irrational. It had happened to her two decades before.

During the Catastrophe in 1948, Mahmoud's mother had been separated from her family. She had gone to Beirut with her aunt, while her parents and siblings fled briefly to southern Lebanon before returning to Palestine. It was only by luck that, two years later, she was reunited with them. Others were not so fortunate. Families and villages were divided. Those who fled had initially thought the war would just last a few months and left most of their belongings behind, only packing bare necessities. Now, several decades into their exile, they were no closer to being reunited with their loved ones or their homeland. Dheeba's aunt was in such a situation, having lived in Beirut with her husband ever since the Catastrophe. Some of her children would never see Palestine. So many others still lived in refugee camps across the region. Mahmoud's village, Tarshiha, was almost totally emptied of its inhabitants, many of whom now resided in perpetuity in Lebanese and Syrian refugee camps. The thought filled him with a deep sadness. Only a few hours away, an entire generation lived waiting for a return to a Palestine they had never known. It could have been him.

Mahmoud ran his fingers through his hair. He watched from the back seat as the bus began to fill up with children, many of them carrying satchels and food packages. It was a rickety old bus from the 1940s, and beneath a coat of paint, applied when the vehicle was passed on to the new municipality for school use and now cracking after years of exposure to the hot Palestinian sun, it was still possible to make out faint English lettering. Inside the bus, the curtains on the windows had half fallen off, no doubt as a result of several generations of maltreatment by school-children. The backs of the seats were covered with names and swear words. Yet, with all its wear and tear, the bus provided Mahmoud with a sense of comfort.

As Mahmoud's schoolmates jostled for window seats, the excitement in the atmosphere was palpable. This trip was the first of its kind in the village. Mahmoud's brothers and sisters had desperately wanted to go, but as the journey would last overnight, it was only suitable for the older children. Mahmoud consoled them that there would be opportunities for them to go soon enough. He had no idea if this was true, and secretly, he was happy that this trip was his to experience alone. No one knew for certain how long the situation would remain this way, creating a sense of urgency. Since the Catastrophe two decades ago, they were always on edge that circumstances might drastically change in a matter of minutes.

Mahmoud was fifteen, born only a few years after the Catastrophe. Although he didn't have many distinct memories from those early years, he recalled a pervasive mood of unease and melancholy during his childhood. The adults talked about people as if they were ghosts, mourning those who were gone but not dead. It was confusing for his young mind. Something bad had happened that had changed everything. Mahmoud couldn't remember when he had first become conscious of it. It seemed to have always been there, as though time itself were determined by this singular point in history. Everything was either before or after the Catastrophe. It was a line separating the normal from the abnormal. Mahmoud had only ever lived the abnormal. From what he could tell, the life 'before' was a better one. Listening to his parents and grandparents, he came to carry as his own their memories of a time that was freer and full of possibility, when people travelled between Nablus, Haifa, Beirut and Damascus, cities then so close to each other that were now so far apart. Notions that today were wild fantasies—to take a bus from Akka to Beirut, crossing at Ras al-Naqoura—were once commonplace. Since the Catastrophe, hard borders had been drawn up and patrolled. Crossing them was unthinkable.

Mahmoud felt a deep longing for that time—a time that he had never lived and yet that he knew so well. It existed all around him in spoken and unspoken stories. He knew details about places that no longer existed, like the villages of Al-Zeeb, Al-Basa and Al-Kabri. Although they were in ruins, he could bring these villages to life in his mind, where he rebuilt them bustling and whole. Mahmoud also knew people he'd never met, like Um Adel, whose lemon tree he was under strict instructions from his parents to take care of. Or the Al-Qadi family, in whose abandoned house he and his friends played hide-and-seek. Theirs wasn't the only home that stood empty, waiting for its owners to return. Many houses had fallen into ruin. A few had been completely erased, leaving only the faintest outlines of foundations. The children were told not to play in these houses. People didn't talk openly about them or their owners, and Mahmoud knew better than to ask too much. He could see the pain in his parents' eyes the few times he brought them up. One of these ruined houses had belonged to his father. What had happened to it and the people who lived there was a well-known story, not just in Tarshiha but across all of the Galilee.

Two and a half decades before the Catastrophe, following the fall of the Ottoman Empire, Palestine had been placed under a British mandate. It was first declared as a temporary arrangement to prepare Palestinians for self-rule. But it soon became clear that this wasn't to be, as the British spent most of their time suppressing Palestinian rebellions and attempts to establish independence. At the same time, the British were facilitating the entry of Zionist settlers into Palestine from Europe, and on the eve of the 1948 war, they more or less handed over their keys and weapons to Zionist militias. Mahmoud knew of an infamous story about a Zionist commander who had bet a British general a bottle of whiskey that Zionist militias could take the city of Haifa in a week. It took them even less than a week. This was in part because the British had quickly retreated and funnelled many of the city's Palestinian inhabitants to the port, where they were swiftly loaded onto boats. One of the first English phrases Mahmoud ever heard had appeared in the anecdotes of visiting relatives: 'To the port, to the port!' The call had been blasted from loudspeakers throughout Haifa and still rang in the ears of its refugees, though there were similar stories across Palestine's other coastal cities. And once the cities had fallen, it was only a matter of time before the villages fell too. Tarshiha was no different. It held out until the autumn of 1948, when it was eventually surrounded and cut off. The Zionist forces launched the attack in the early hours of the morning. Most of the men were in the hills, forming a line of defence around the village. The few who bore weapons carried only their old muskets from the Ottoman era. The rest were armed with farming equipment and sheer courage.

Rather than invade on foot, the enemy used British planes to bomb them from the skies. As the village burned, the men broke their line of defence and ran towards their houses in the hope of saving their wives and children. They returned to scenes of utter devastation. Over half of the homes had been destroyed, and most of the villagers were forced to flee. Those who stayed did so to bury their dead. Mahmoud's father, Kamel, was among those who remained. He had been in the fields with the rest of the men when the bomb had fallen, while his pregnant wife and child were at the family home. They were martyred, as were nine other members of his family.

After the bombing, the survivors retreated to the mountains. Some continued on to Lebanon; others stayed nearby but hidden. Nowhere seemed safe. Tarshiha was the last stronghold of resistance in the region, and its defeat signalled the fall of the entire Galilee. The Arab Salvation Army quickly retreated to Lebanon, and other pockets of resistance collapsed. And with that, Palestine was wiped off the map. It was a catastrophe that continued to reverberate. Even now, two decades on, they hadn't recovered.

Today, Kamel barely talked about the fall of Tarshiha. To Mahmoud's disappointment, his father would always find a way to avoid his questions, preferring not to re-open the past. 'Forget it. What happened, happened,' he would say resolutely. And so, Mahmoud learned what he could from his other family members, actively seeking out those conversations. His mother and his grand-mother were the most skilled and comprehensive story-tellers. For them, it was a cathartic practice. 'If we don't remember, it'll be gone forever,' his mother would tell him. Mahmoud hung on to their words, determined to take up his duty to remember, to understand. But despite his craving to know more, he found that stories of the Catastrophe rested heavily and painfully on his mind. He could imagine them vividly, with anguish, as if they were his own memories. They overshadowed the present and blurred distinctions in time and between generations.

Kamel's reticence was in keeping with his personality. He had a stern exterior and was never overly affectionate with his children. This stood in stark comparison with Mahmoud's mother, who never held back when it came to kissing, hugging and playing. Dheeba also adopted the role of family mediator, whether between the children themselves or between Kamel and the children, asking him to let them off their chores or allow them to stay up late. In a way, the two parents balanced each other out. But beneath his sternness, Mahmoud knew that his father was a kind man. It was obvious in the way that he succumbed to his mother's mediations, and in the special interest he took in his children's education. Every day, he asked them one by one what they had done at school.

In the wider community, Kamel's reputation was that of a respectable and hardworking fallah. They weren't a wealthy family, nor did they own hundreds of dunams of land. But they made ends meet and took pride in the fact that they were from one of the village's original families, which could trace its ancestors back hundreds of years. Before becoming known as Hawari, the family had been part of the Shreh clan. The name Hawari had come later, after a chance meeting with the North African Hawara tribe. One of the family's ancestors, a young boy at the time, was drowning in a reservoir near the village. While passing by, members of the Hawara tribe heard his cries and rescued him from certain death. Henceforth, the boy became known as 'Al-Hawari', and his descendants adopted the name.

Tarshiha, the village, was another source of pride, and it too had a naming story, which Mahmoud revelled in telling. Assuming a deep, authoritative voice, he would start the tale many centuries ago with a man called Shiha, known as a fierce fighter in the Galilee, who one day became embroiled in a sword fight at the top of a mountain. Alas, despite Shiha's fearsome reputation, his opponent cut off his head. 'Tar ras Shiha.' *Shiha's head flew.* It was a gruesome anecdote but was usually received with laughter. And it wasn't just Mahmoud who liked to tell it; each villager had their own version and added different details. The tale was very popular, particularly amongst the children. Whether it was true or not didn't really matter.

Regardless of its beginnings, Tarshiha soon became an important village for its rich agriculture and strategic position in the Upper Galilee. Surrounded by valleys and mountains, it had plenty of access to water and other natural resources. Many of the villagers relied on the land and lived seasonally. The village was famous for its craftsmen—its many blacksmiths, goldsmiths, carpenters and stone masons. But it was also known for its artists, and throughout its streets, music was often heard tinkling out of doorways. Tarshiha was a mixed village, populated by both Christians and Muslims. Here, the divisions between the two communities were less pronounced than in some other villages, and Christian families and Muslim families lived side by side. On Christmas, Mahmoud would visit his Christian friends' homes, while the reverse would happen on Eid. Still, marriages across the two religions were rare.

Mahmoud was the product of a mixed marriage of a different sort. Kamel had married his second wife, Dheeba, a few years after the Catastrophe. She was a Bedouin and he was a fallah, but while such a marriage was uncommon, the match was not resisted by either side. Kamel's father and mother were from respectable families and had good reputations, and Dheeba's father and Kamel were friends. Mahmoud's grandmother enjoyed telling him how much his parents liked each other, that theirs was a love story as opposed to an arranged marriage. It was strange for Mahmoud to think of his parents' lives before they married. Stranger still was the discovery that his father had had a wife and child before his mother and his siblings. Mahmoud couldn't quite remember who had told him. It had never been hidden; it was just a fact from the time 'before' that didn't need dwelling on.

Yet Mahmoud did dwell on this fact and on how different things might have been. What if his father's first wife and child hadn't been killed? It made Mahmoud uneasy knowing that his very existence was predicated on that trauma. His generation was the first only to have known tragedy, to be defined by it. He wondered if that would be the case forever, if Palestinianness would always be intricately linked with the Catastrophe. These internal conversations were exhausting and left him more confused. He taught himself to compartmentalise history; it wasn't good to play this kind of 'what if' game for too long. Instead, Mahmoud would indulge in another practice of the imagination. He pictured what his land would be like had the Catastrophe not taken place. From the nostalgic stories of his relatives, he put together an image of Palestine, free and unoccupied—a vision that gave him temporary reprieve from the present. The troubling thing was that in these moments of invention, he felt more at home than in his reality. It was then that he would feel a mixture of jealousy and bitterness towards the previous generation. They had had it, they knew a life that was better than this, and they had lost it.

Mahmoud's family lived in a simple house in the lower neighbourhood of the village. Like many houses in Tarshiha, it had once belonged to a family who had since become refugees in Lebanon. The house was composed of a small kitchen and two rooms; one housed the six children, while the other functioned as both Kamel and Dheeba's bedroom and the living room. The children slept on the floor on mattresses, which they would pile up in a corner every morning. Their parents' room was divided into the sleeping area and the living area, which had a coffee table and two sofas, positioned around the radio. When the children were older, a new living room was built, in which to host guests. Next to the house was a garden and an orchard, where Mahmoud's mother planted vegetables and fruit trees. They kept various animals, including chickens and goats, which roamed freely. The home was simple and modest.

Mahmoud's family made a living from their tobacco fields and olive trees, surviving on their own yield of vegetables and grains. Everyone worked to make sure there was enough food to go round, including the children. Mahmoud started helping his parents at the age of five. Of all his tasks, his favourite was collecting milk from the fields. His mother would send him and his younger brother Mohammed off on two donkeys loaded with empty containers. Mahmoud would ride his favourite donkey, Abu Saber—named for his endless patience. The donkeys knew the route to the fields and would slowly make their way to where Mahmoud's father and uncle took care of the goats. Once the containers were filled with milk, the boys would climb back onto the donkeys and set off home by themselves. At such a young age, Mahmoud felt an important sense of responsibility. Not only did he have to make sure the milk arrived, but he also had to take care of his younger brother, keeping an eye out to check that he stayed on the donkey.

Tobacco was a labour-intensive crop that required everyone's help. During the harvest season, the children would wake up a few hours before sunrise and spend three hours in the field, before rushing home, washing and changing for school. When classes ended and the children had returned home, they would then spend a few hours stringing up tobacco leaves before doing their homework. As Mahmoud grew older, the planting of tobacco coincided with exam time. He would take his books with him to the fields, reading in the horse cart both there and on the way back. It was hard balancing the work of a fallah with school. Sometimes, Mahmoud felt jealous of children in the village who got to spend their summers at camps. Yet for the most part, he was content with his life, and moreover he was reminded that going to school was a real privilege. Mahmoud's parents insisted that all their children finish their schooling. Part of his mother's conviction was rooted in the fact that she herself had not had the opportunity to go to school. It was unusual for Bedouin, and in particular girls, to spend a long time in institutional education. Rather, they were taught on the land, learning to survive the harsh realities that came with the Bedouin lifestyle. A few years after starting school, Mahmoud discovered, to his great surprise, that his mother could neither read nor write. Even so, she had always supervised Mahmoud and his brother in their homework, asking them to check their spellings and to write more neatly, never letting on that she was almost illiterate. He once asked her how she could check their writing if she had never been to school. 'I don't need to read to know if you are doing your homework or not!' she replied defensively, prompting Mahmoud to feel ashamed. He realised later that she had learned to judge their work from the form of the letters without any knowledge of the alphabet itself. There were so many other things that she had miraculously managed to navigate. Like the rest of her generation, she had had to learn basic Hebrew very quickly to be able to deal with the authorities. Not understanding a soldier's command could be deadly. There were too many stories about people who had failed to understand orders to stop or stand still and who were consequently shot dead.

The importance of schooling was also inculcated in Mahmoud from a young age by his father. Kamel felt that there was no future in working the land and that education was the only way forward. 'The Zionists are going to take it all,' he would say, matter-of-factly. Mahmoud was disappointed by what seemed like his father's succumbence to indefinite Zionist occupation. As if to hammer home his misgivings, Kamel often complained loudly about his backache and cursed the fallah lifestyle. Mahmoud could tell it was a ruse, but it made him sad that his father felt he had to dissuade them from his way of life. For Kamel, it was simply a matter of survival that Mahmoud and his siblings focus on their formal education. And it didn't stop at school—there was also university to consider. Mahmoud wasn't averse to the idea; the prospect of studying any topic of his choosing excited him. But to his father's dismay, Mahmoud wasn't interested in pursuing what Kamel considered to be a practical degree, like engineering or law. He had just learned of a discipline called archaeology—the study of ruins from the past. His heart became set on it, and he came to spend hours in the hills around the village picking up coins and pieces of old pots, imagining their origins, making up conclusions about ancient civilisations that lay buried beneath.

As well as being studious, Mahmoud was a resourceful child and always found novel ways to make pocket money.

At the age of ten, he made a discovery that allowed him to earn a steady income over the summer months. He had spotted a group of Jewish settlers from a nearby moshav gathered around a bush, and as he approached, he could see that they were picking its small berries. Loud complaints rang out, since the berry-pickers found themselves getting scratched by the bush's thorns throughout their endeavour. Mahmoud offered to pick the berries in return for a payment. He didn't understand why they wanted the berries or even know them to be edible—he had certainly never seen anyone in the village eating them. After a few months, his curiosity got the better of him, and he asked one of the settlers what the berries were used for. He was told that they were pickled, in much the same way that Palestinians pickled olives.

Hamoud, Mahmoud's maternal grandfather, later elaborated that these were called caper berries and delved into a longer explanation about the different food customs of the settlers. Mahmoud was in awe of the vast knowledge of his grandfather, who towered above him even when sitting and would narrate stories about having fought the British during the Great Revolt. His grandmother, Hamda, would chime in with tales of the Turks and life under the Ottoman Empire. Mahmoud savoured his trips to see his grandparents in the upper part of the village, where they lived with other Bedouin families who had sought shelter and a new home.

Before his mother's parents had moved to Tarshiha, Mahmoud remembered visiting them in their old stone house in the north. Although his memories were a little hazy, he could recall having loved those visits. The house had been built by his grandfather, close to the border with Lebanon. His mother would take him and his baby brother to visit, and while it wasn't very far, they often stayed overnight. From Tarshiha, they would take the Akka bus down to Al-Kabri junction, where they would then wait for any car heading north. Sometimes, they were lucky enough to come upon one within an hour. Other times, it took longer. From Al-Kabri, the road continued north for six and a half kilometres before veering eastwards. Seven kilometres further, they would reach Mahmoud's grandparents' house.

These trips were always an adventure for little Mahmoud. Looking back, he realised that it must have been quite an effort for his mother to travel with two young children to this remote part of the north. Unlike in Tarshiha, which was slowly becoming modernised, the stone house had no electricity or running water. It was set back from the main road, up a steep dirt track, surrounded by nothing but mountains and wadis. His grandparents lived on gas light and water drawn from the well. The house was built in such a way as to retain heat from the wood burner during the cold months and stay cool in the summer months.

As Bedouin, Mahmoud's mother's family spoke in a manner that was distinct from the fallaheen in Tarshiha. They had a thicker accent, pronouncing 'k' sounds as 'ch' and 'q' sounds as 'g', and sometimes used different words entirely. The Bedouin were mostly herders and shepherds, with animals providing the main source of their livelihood. Traditionally, they moved with the seasons across their lands, living in tents made from goat hair. Later, many would settle in houses, leading inevitably to the erosion of some of their traditions. Mahmoud knew that they were sometimes looked down upon by others for being poorer and less formally educated. His mother's social status in Tarshiha was better than that of her relatives because she had married into a fallah family. But the village was still rife with prejudice. Some of the villagers even sought to remind everyone who was *from* the village and who had *come* to the village. Mahmoud felt it was an unfair distinction. It wasn't by choice that they had ended up in a village that wasn't their own. And neither was it by choice that they had nowhere to live but in the homes of those who had been killed or exiled several decades before. It was a cruel irony, and in the end, they were all forced to live with ghosts of the past.

When Mahmoud and his siblings were not in the fields or at school, they often played in the cobbled streets of Tarshiha with the rest of the children. The alleyways and bombed houses provided plenty of cover for hiding and chasing each other. Apart from the usual street games, there were also more exciting activities. Tarshiha was considered a centre of commerce and social life for the neighbouring villages. Capitalising on this position, a man from Akka came once a month to the village with a projector, erecting a large white sheet in the main square on which to show the latest films and newsreels. The adults would bring their chairs from home and pay a small fee to watch, while the children would sit in front of them on the floor, or sometimes on small stools. American Westerns, featuring the likes of John Wayne, were popular on these occasions, the horseback chases and gun battles being a source of great entertainment. Mahmoud and his friends sat as close as possible to the front in the hope that they would find the cowboys' bullet casings. They never did. The films they watched also gave them epic backstories for the games they played in the streets. 'Cowboys and Indians' was a recurring theme. For some reason, the upper neighbourhood always played the role of the cowboys while the lower neighbourhood were the Indians; the two sides never switched. Mahmoud was in the lower neighbourhood. It was his idea to fashion toy weapons from the tobacco stalks left over in the fields. Meanwhile, the 'cowboys' rode on wooden sticks to mimic horses. More often than not, the upper neighbourhood demanded to win the game like the cowboys did in the films. Mahmoud and his kinsmen held out—the fight would be to the bitter end and would be determined by the last child standing.

The roar of the rickety bus engine jolted Mahmoud back to the present. He looked to the window to wave a final goodbye to his mother, before turning round to his uncle Nawaf, who was sitting next to him. Grinning, Nawaf put his arm around Mahmoud. 'Ready, ibn ukhti, my sister's son?' he asked. The two jokingly and tenderly referred to each other by their blood relationship, even though it wasn't particularly unusual for an uncle and a nephew to be of the same age. Besides being relatives and classmates, Mahmoud and Nawaf were good friends.

They had discussed this trip for weeks, spending hours arguing about which would be the most exciting part. Mahmoud was most fascinated by Jerusalem. He had been once before as a young child but didn't remember it well. Everything else he knew from avid reading and listening, awed as he was by the city's history. It had withstood invasion after invasion, from the Crusaders to the Zionists. Mahmoud and Nawaf traded stories that they heard, sharing details and together painting a picture of Palestine. The more they heard, the more familiar it became. It wasn't long before Mahmoud was talking with confident familiarity about places that he had never visited.

Mahmoud also learned fairly quickly that many of his schoolbooks couldn't be trusted to teach him his history. It was outside of school that he sought books or papers that described what Palestine had been like before. He was captivated by stories of ancient civilisations and by the steadfastness of buildings that had survived a multitude of occupations. But it wasn't easy to get his hands on this literature. He and all the other Palestinians who lived in the territories occupied in 1948 were under Israeli military rule, which meant strict martial law. It was as repressive as it was suffocating. Every aspect of their lives was monitored and watched. Going to neighbouring villages or towns required a permit from the local police station. Under such tyrannical surveillance, Mahmoud and his friends devoured whatever forbidden books they could get their hands on, often resorting to hiding them under mattresses and in hidden cracks in the walls.

Once, Mahmoud's father had discovered the hidden literature and scolded him. 'You're risking getting in trouble, and for what? Books?' If his intention was to frighten Mahmoud, it didn't work; nor did he force Mahmoud to get rid of the books. Instead, Mahmoud was imbued with a renewed determination to know even more. He particularly hunted for books about the Arab world and by famous Arab authors. The military regime imposed strict censorship restrictions, and it was forbidden to import Arab books. Yet, somehow, they managed to find a precious few. These snippets of writing were enough to set Mahmoud's imagination free. He visualised a world lived by those only a few decades before him, where he could jump on a bus to Beirut or Damascus, or study in the great universities of Cairo or Baghdad. He knew he was a part of this world. Yet he could barely travel around the Galilee, let alone visit the greatest capitals that history had ever seen. He was always dragged back to the painful reality of physical borders and enforced separation.

It wasn't only books that were banned—Arabic radio stations were also not permitted. Those who had radios were often monitored. But it didn't stop them. Mahmoud and his friends, like so many, were enthralled by Gamal Abdel Nasser, the charismatic Egyptian president, who spouted new ideas of revolutionary Pan-Arabism in the face of continuing colonialism. Whenever a speech by Nasser was scheduled on the radio, the whole extended family gathered around to listen. Another of Mahmoud's uncles, Ahmed, was particularly besotted with the Egyptian leader. He would stand up at the beginning of every speech as a sign of respect, clapping and shouting enthusiastically every few minutes, until eventually everyone would implore him to keep quiet so they could listen. Naturally, someone would always keep an eye out for potential spies and collaborators. It was a serious matter. The year before, during the last war, Mahmoud's neighbour Abu Mohammed had been listening to his radio. Upon hearing of the Arab armies' defeat, he had gone into a rage, smashing the radio and cursing the Zionists at the top of his voice. It was no wonder that the next day, he was taken to the local police station for interrogation. He emerged a day later, somewhat subdued but clearly resolute. If nothing else, this incident confirmed that informers were widespread and their network substantial. Many people were so desperate for permits and licenses to make ends meet that they were susceptible to sharing or even making up information. Others, of course, were collaborators by choice. They picked the winning side and abandoned their own. Not only were people carted off for interrogation, but several were also routinely publicly humiliated by the Zionist forces. They could be insulted or beaten in the streets for no reason whatsoever. Even children younger than Mahmoud were exposed to this cruelty.

For Mahmoud, the radio didn't only provide clandestine political education. It was also a form of communication between separated families and friends. One programme in particular allowed Palestinian refugees in Syria and Lebanon to submit greetings and news to their loved ones still in Palestine. Deaths and details of funerals were announced, as well as marriages, births and even school graduations. These bulletins were a particular favourite of Mahmoud's sisters, Eftikhar, Nizar and Entisar. They would ask him to turn the volume up so that everyone in the house could hear. Every time someone from Tarshiha or the Hawari family submitted a message, the girls shouted for their father to come and listen. They waited on tenterhooks for a familiar message across the airwaves. Kamel, meanwhile, hovered nearby with sadness, his head drooping and his arms crossed. Mahmoud would notice as the colour from his father's face slowly drained, as if he were listening to eerie voices from beyond the grave. But these people on the radio were not dead. 'They're not even that far away,' Mahmoud thought to himself.

The children on the bus cheered as they passed by their school. The trip meant a few days off from their usual classes. Mahmoud, however, felt a pang of nausea as he looked at the school building. It was adorned with Israeli flags—a constant presence in the school, and even more so during state holidays. Every year, the school was forced to celebrate Israeli Independence Day, inducing in Mahmoud a particularly acute feeling of pain. When he was younger, he hadn't thought much of it. It was a nationwide holiday, and all the young children looked forward to the break from studying. But as he grew older, he began to notice the atmosphere of melancholy that would set in among the adults. They weren't celebrating. Their heads hung low.

On the day itself, the children took part in activities such as painting flags, playing sports and reciting poetry. The day's events started with a school-wide rendition of 'My Country's Independence Day':

'Eid istiqlal biladi	*On my country's Independence Day*
Gharrad al-tayr al-shadi	*The birds chirp and rejoice*
Wa 'ammat al-farha al-buldan	*Joy prevails in the towns*
Hatta al-sahl wal-wadi	*Even in the plains and the wadi*
Al-sha'b yughanni farhan mitahanni	*The people sing happily*
Yahlalu al-tarteel fee 'eid Isra'eel	*They celebrate Israel's holiday*
Wa damti ya biladi	*My blood, my country*

The school invited guests, including the children's families and the local Israeli police chief. The latter delivered the same speech every year, emphasising the importance of being loyal and grateful to the Zionist state. Mahmoud thought it a perverse demand that they should be forced to celebrate their own dispossession. Last year, he and his friends had held several secret meetings after school to plan a revolt against the festivities. Feeling incredibly grown up and enigmatic, they vowed to disrupt the celebration by tearing up as many Israeli flags as possible and singing the Palestinian national anthem, 'Mawtini', at the ceremony. Then the war had broken out and everything was cancelled. Mahmoud and his friends never got to carry out their grand subversive plot.

On the morning of the war, the headmaster had delivered an announcement to the whole school, a tinge of shame creeping over his face as he spoke. He explained that in wartime conditions, they had to stand by the state. It was a test for the Arab citizens to show the occupiers that they too could belong to Israel. His words didn't have the desired effect on Mahmoud and his friends, who were certain that this was the revolution that would finally lead to liberation. But their excitement didn't last, and it wasn't long before the war ended. Like Abu Mohammed, they had also been listening to the radio when the Arab armies were swiftly defeated. It was unbelievable. Mahmoud had been sure that the Zionist occupation would be overthrown by Nasser and his comrades. He was crushed by devastation and humiliation like he had never known before.

Mahmoud had confided his grief in his uncle Ibrahim, one of Nawaf's older brothers, who was studying at the Hebrew University in Jerusalem and was active in the Arab students' movement. Unlike many of the adults, Ibrahim was always ready to talk politics. When he spoke, he became animated, passionate and at times angry. It was from Ibrahim that Mahmoud began to understand more complex political issues. He managed to put into words what Mahmoud could not. 'This is a different occupation we are facing, ya Mahmoud,' he would say definitively. Ibrahim's experience at university had changed him. While he had suffered under military rule in the Galilee too, Jerusalem felt like a frontline. On one of his visits home, Ibrahim explained to Mahmoud that Palestinian students at the university were treated with suspicion and contempt by their Jewish Israeli peers, sometimes even leading to direct violent confrontations. Worse yet, many of the university professors were former army generals who had taken part in the Catastrophe, and, inevitably, in many of its atrocities. Ibrahim described his shock and disgust when he discovered that one of his professors had participated in the final operation to cleanse the Galilee of its Palestinian inhabitants. He left the class soon after that discovery.

Ibrahim also informed Mahmoud that there were plans for more ethnic cleansing. 'You were too young, but I remember Kafr Qassem well,' Ibrahim recalled with an air of seniority, despite only being six years older. Mahmoud had already heard about Kafr Qassem. It was a story everyone knew and feared. Situated on a hilltop in the Triangle area adjacent to the West Bank, the village was right on the armistice line. In 1956, the Israeli government had been concerned about the villages in the Triangle and their potential for disobedience. Giving the excuse that Palestinian fighters were using the area to hide, they placed it under tighter restrictions, including strict curfews. One day, the Zionist colonel in charge of the area decided to change the curfew from 9.00 p.m. to 5.00 p.m. without informing the local inhabitants. He instructed soldiers to shoot on sight anyone breaking the new curfew. Many officers decided to allow latecomers to return home, usually after a beating. The officer overseeing Kafr Qassem, however, was merciless. Ibrahim told Mahmoud of the first two to be killed. Ahmad Fariq and Ali Taha had been approaching the village checkpoint on their bicycles when they were ordered by the soldiers to get off and line up. The soldiers opened fire. It was said that when the two bodies were recovered, they were riddled with bullets. Others met similar fates, like Fatma Sarsur, who was eight months pregnant and returning from the olive harvest. By the time the soldiers had finished their killing spree, forty-eight villagers had been murdered, among them seventeen children. The military censorship prevented anything from being published about the massacre. But the story still managed to seep its way into every village in Palestine, just as the massacre at Deir Yassin had several decades before.

Mahmoud couldn't quite recall when Ibrahim, Nawaf and the rest of his mother's family had come to Tarshiha. But he did remember that it had been all of a sudden. It was clear that something bad had happened. A few years later, he asked his mother when they would be visiting his grandparents' stone house in the north. 'We won't be,' she replied abruptly. He didn't ask again. Only when he was older did he learn what had happened from his uncle. Ibrahim had been a young boy when the soldiers came to their house in the early hours of the morning. The family awoke to the sounds of shouting and banging on the door. Ibrahim's father, ever calm, got up and dressed before opening it. The soldiers barged in, shouting in Hebrew and demanding that the adult men line up outside the house. Mahmoud's grandfather and uncle were taken

26

away swiftly, leaving Ibrahim, his younger siblings and their mother to pack up as many things as they could. The soldiers who stayed behind loaded them onto a truck along with their belongings. They were driven forty kilometres south and then dumped on the side of the road like sacks of rubbish. In a nearby village, they sought refuge with a distant relative. Ibrahim's father and brother were released after a few days of detention and beatings. Reunited with the rest of the family, they now found themselves homeless. They were told that their house and land had been confiscated for the security of the state. The stone house was sealed off with barbed wire, and the family was warned by the authorities not to set foot on the land again.

Mahmoud could see the colour rising in Ibrahim's face as he recounted this story to him and Nawaf. He could tell that his uncle felt guilty that the army hadn't taken him along with his father and older brother. Ibrahim was probably considered too young by the soldiers to be a threat. Mahmoud couldn't understand why deep sadness and grief were somehow more manageable than feelings of guilt—something they all felt as survivors of the Catastrophe. It was sometimes hard to reckon with the atrocities they had escaped when their survival itself was constantly invalidated by the authorities. At school, Mahmoud was told how lucky he was to be living in a democratic and Western state, unlike their Arab neighbours living under despots and in miserable conditions. His schoolbooks described the foundation of the state of Israel as a miracle—a flower blooming in the barren desert. Before Israel, they were nothing but uncivilised Bedouin—a term used by the authorities as an insult—who didn't know how to cultivate the land. In lessons, the children were shown photographs of what appeared to be arid land and destitute people from before the establishment of Israel. Mahmoud asked his father later if it was true. Kamel replied that if the photograph had only been taken from the other direction, it would show the bustling international port of Yaffa. But that history was deliberately erased. 'Don't believe them when they tell you that before Israel there was nothing,' he told Mahmoud.

Mahmoud knew his father was right. He simply had to look around him to see that his ancestors had toiled this very land for centuries. They were its caretakers and knew how to farm soil that seemed infertile and dry to the foreign eye. They knew what to plant and when to plant it. They built terraces into steep slopes and planted olive trees that outlived them. Their natural rhythm of life was tied to the land, and this was passed on to their descendants. The occupiers had since tried to make the land alien to its original inhabitants, so that even they would question whether or not they belonged. They planted European trees, covering the ruins of Palestinian villages with thick, unrelenting forests. They built new roads that cut through mountains and disrupted routes used for centuries.

It wasn't just the landscape that the Zionists wanted to change. It was also the people, those who had survived the Catastrophe. These people were living proof that something had existed before, and they needed to be dealt with. But the occupiers couldn't simply get rid of them, as they had done with the others. Instead they made life difficult—so difficult that survival was all the people could focus on—and banished them to the fringes of the new state. They labelled them a dangerous minority who had to be watched. They instilled a fear so acute that it forced amnesia in many.

Mahmoud felt the bus slowing down. Glancing out the window, he noticed that they were approaching the crossing point into the West Bank. The sight wasn't particularly remarkable—a makeshift checkpoint, an array of sandbags and barrels guarded by Israeli soldiers only a few years older than Mahmoud. They had their guns pointed in the other direction, their fingers on the triggers, poised and ready for an attack of any kind. The bus stopped at the request of a soldier, who boarded and checked the paperwork carried by one of the teachers. The children fell silent. Mahmoud felt Nawaf grab his arm. Without looking at him, Mahmoud whispered under his breath, 'Don't worry, it's just a routine check.' But the presence of the Israeli soldier was enough to entirely change the atmosphere on the bus. Mahmoud observed as the soldier quickly glanced around, appearing not to find anything particularly interesting or suspicious about a group of Arab schoolchildren. The soldier got off and waved them on. Mahmoud felt Nawaf breathe a sigh of relief. Soon after the checkpoint, the classmates relaxed and started to sing a medley of folk songs. But Mahmoud wasn't in the mood for singing. He ran his fingers through his hair and pressed his face against the glass of the window, staring off into the distance.

The vast landscape before him was full of vivid colours. It was different to the green mountains of the Galilee that he was used to. As he peered out the window, Mahmoud noticed something strange in the distance. On approach, he realised that it was a burned-out Jordanian tank. Mahmoud felt a sharp pain in his chest. Hundreds of thoughts started to race through his whirring mind. *How could they have lost? How could they have given up what was left of Palestine so easily?* He pictured the Arab leaders who had assured them of liberation and a united Arab people. He hated them. They had promised so much and had been so convincing. Tears started to roll down Mahmoud's face, and he was suddenly overwhelmed by a powerful urge to spit. As his saliva slid down the window, Mahmoud turned around surreptitiously to make sure no one had noticed, before returning his gaze to the land outside. He caught a glimpse of a house perched on a hilltop, and as the bus drew closer, he refocused his eyes and began to make out its details. It had no door and the shutters had half fallen off, or had perhaps even been ripped off. The garden around the building was in disarray. Looking more closely, Mahmoud could see tell-tale signs of violence; the side of the house was splattered with bullet holes. Mahmoud's stomach clenched, as he wondered who the house's owners were and whether they had survived the war.

Mahmoud turned away as the bus passed the hilltop, but his thoughts remained fixated on the house. Its simplicity felt familiar. He immediately thought of his grandparents' stone house, sitting empty and lonely on the mountainside. History was repeating itself with the same patterns of tragedy. As the house receded from view, Mahmoud leaned back in his seat, wondering what it might feel like not to live under the shadow of a constant catastrophe. He let his mind wander back to his family's stone house, imagining himself living there, free and untinged by tragedy. Here, there were no feelings of sadness or guilt, nor was there anything to grieve. In this imagined place, Mahmoud felt himself.

DHEEBA

Dheeba stood with the other parents as the children piled onto the bus. Instinctively, she looked towards the back of the vehicle, where she knew Mahmoud would be sitting, no doubt soon to be followed by the other boisterous boys in his class. Catching his smiling face peering at her through the window, she felt herself relax. He was always easy to spot, his ringleted mass of hair making up for the fact that he wasn't as tall as the other boys. At first, it had bewildered Dheeba that her son allowed his hair to grow into a large, curly ball. It was a foreign style, no doubt influenced by the foreign music he was so obsessed with. She implored him to cut it on a weekly basis. 'It's so messy, yimma, why not keep it short and smart?' Her pleas were pointless. Mahmoud was stubborn by nature, and by now he had reached the age when adolescence pushed closely against adulthood. While other children usually felt awkward and uncomfortable, Mahmoud's curly hair blessed him with an unshakable confidence, and in the end, Dheeba gave up nagging him. Besides, he was doing well at school, worked hard in the fields and took good care of his siblings; since he was the eldest, the task of keeping them entertained naturally fell to him. He played them music, read to them and invented all kinds of games. One of their particular favourites was play-acting as a rock band. Mahmoud would gather household items and assemble his siblings in a line, giving each an instrument—a broom for a guitar, a pot and stick for a drum set. They always made such a racket that eventually Dheeba would yell at them to go play outside. Generally, apart from the usual squabbles, the children got along. They were six: three boys and three girls. Even though boys were customarily preferred since they would carry on the family name, Dheeba was delighted that she had both.

Dheeba kept her gaze focused on Mahmoud, whose attention had since drifted elsewhere. He took after her side of the family—there was no doubt about that. His eyes, his mouth and that hair were clearly Bedouin features. Even though she had married a fallah, Dheeba fiercely retained her Bedouin identity. She was from the Samniyeh tribe, whose lands extended across Wadi Karkara in the Upper Western Galilee. Her father was a well-respected Bedouin dignitary, known for having fought in the resistance against the English, and then later against the Zionists. Dheeba had grown up on the border with Lebanon, living in a beit sha'ar—goat-hair tent—until her father had built them a stone house. By this time, many among the Samniyeh tribe were building and settling in stone houses. Dheeba's family home was situated between mountains on one side and a wadi on the other, with very few neighbours. There was a well nearby and plenty of grazing land for the animals. As a girl, she would spend most of her days with her siblings, taking care of the animals or helping her mother in the house. They were a large family; her mother had ten children in all, although Dheeba only grew up with half of them. The rest were still very young when she left home, and one was even born when she had started to have her own children. Thus, her youngest brother, Nawaf, was the same age as her eldest son.

As Dheeba stood waiting for the bus to depart, she felt the crisp, spring air against her calves. It was her favourite time of year. The land was at its greenest, and the Galilee in particular was the lushest part of the country. Beginning north of the Jezreel Valley, it spanned the whole northern part of Palestine, with Nazareth in the south, Akka on the coast, and Safad in the east. The Lower Galilee was much less dramatic than the Upper Galilee, which boasted fertile mountain ranges and snowy peaks in the winter. This was Dheeba's home; her ancestors had dwelt on these lands for centuries, and while growing up, she couldn't have imagined being anywhere else. Springtime still reminded her of her teenage years. Dheeba and her sisters, along with their friends from the neighbouring village of Iqrit, had often walked down to Wadi Karkara, where they would picnic by the stream that flowed down from Lebanon, through the Galilee mountains and into the Mediterranean Sea just south of Ras al-Naqoura. The stream was ice cold year round, but Dheeba would always dip her feet in. The freezing rush made her feel alive. She shivered slightly at the memory, wrapping her arms around herself. She couldn't remember the last time she had gone to the wadi. Ever since her family's displacement, she didn't go north at all. It was too painful to return to land that had been forcefully seized from them by the

Zionists. Besides, these days, with the children and the harvests, she didn't have time for those kinds of activities.

Kamel had not joined her to see Mahmoud off. 'He'll be back in a few days,' he told her. Yet Dheeba was certain that her husband would be the first one waiting at the entrance of the village on the bus's return. She could tell that he restrained his feelings out of fear of opening up too much. With practised self-control, he kept his emotions bubbling just below the surface, expending considerable effort to avoid revealing them. The war had caused so much devastation; houses were bombed, whole villages destroyed. But there was also a devastation that was not visible to the naked eye, the kind that wreaked havoc in minds and hearts. Like so many others, Kamel was traumatised. Everyone knew what had happened to Tarshiha—and what had happened to the Hawari family in particular. They had suffered the most deaths in the village, losing eleven of their own. The martyrs were mostly girls and women, spanning across three generations. Their home was bombed to rubble.

Fawziya, Kamel's sister, was the first corpse they had pulled from the ruins. One of the few whose body hadn't been charred, she lay still amidst the debris as if she were sleeping, her famed blond hair seemingly untouched. Yet her form held no breath, no life. Kamel's other sister, Fatma, was recovered next, miraculously alive. They dragged her out by her arms while she screamed that her legs had been severed. They hadn't, in fact, but she was unable to feel them. Among the other victims of the bombing were Kamel's first wife, Su'ad, and their baby son. When their bodies were pulled from the rubble, they were burnt beyond recognition. Dheeba had heard that Kamel had wrapped them in his white kuffiyeh and buried them at the site of the bombed house. The burial was quicker than Islamic tradition stipulated; war cared for neither mourning nor ceremony.

It was said that few cried during the Catastrophe—there had simply been no time. People were either fleeing or trying to pick up the pieces from the ashes of their homes. Tarshiha was nearly decimated in the bombing. So few of its residents remained that it was not long before Zionists came to take over the village. They were mostly Romanian Jews, and they settled in the houses of those who had fled. The surviving villagers who remained in Tarshiha were contained in one area of the village, where they stayed for several months under the watchful eye of Zionist soldiers. Then, soon after their arrival, the Romanians left Tarshiha and established a moshav settlement nearby. Other villagers who had been hiding in the surrounding hills trickled back in.

Even though some time had passed, Dheeba suspected that Kamel still hadn't properly mourned the loss of his family. She often wondered about Su'ad, about what she had been like and her relationship with Kamel. It was hard to imagine that her husband had been married before. Dheeba was not jealous, but she did fear being second best. Although Kamel had never made her feel anything other than loved and respected, his sorrow in their first year of marriage had been palpable. She had been unsure of how to help him through his grief, especially as it wasn't in his nature to open up and share his intimate emotions. However, to Dheeba's relief, much of her husband's sadness had dissipated upon the arrival of their first son. Mahmoud had brought new purpose into the house and served as a joyful distraction. Everyone else then had been having babies too, it seemed. After so much loss, it was only natural to fill the void with new life. Mahmoud had arrived one year after Dheeba's marriage to Kamel and five years after the Catastrophe. The rest of the children followed in quick succession, one after the other, with a new addition to the family nearly every year.

Dheeba turned to listen to the rest of the parents chattering as they waited for the bus to load. It was the first time in almost two decades that anyone from the village was going to the newly occupied territories. They were reminiscing about the last time they had been to the West Bank, only a few hours' drive from Tarshiha and yet totally cut off from them ever since the Catastrophe. Before 1948, it had been an entirely different world. They had still been occupied—by the British—but it had been a different kind of occupation. They knew that, eventually, the occupiers would leave, once they had bled the land dry of all that they could. The Zionists were not the same.

Mahmoud hated it when his mother compared the two occupations. 'They're both colonisers,' he would tell her defiantly. Dheeba knew that, but she also knew that life had been slightly easier under the British. After the war, people couldn't believe what had happened to them. It was temporary, their leaders told them. But with each passing day, the impermanence of things became harder to believe. Palestine had been severed into disjointed fragments. The armistice lines imposed after the Catastrophe meant that even some villages were split in two. The Palestinians on the Israeli side, like those here in the Galilee, had been placed under a harsh military regime. They had suffered for nearly two decades under intense surveillance and repression. Then came the second war. There was a brief glimmer of hope that the Arabs would bring an end to their occupation, that they would finally be reunited with their friends and family in the camps. Dheeba had been less sanguine than the others, and her pessimism proved warranted. The Zionists quickly occupied the rest of historic Palestine, as well as parts of Egypt and Syria. The reunification was bittersweet. Palestine's lands were together once again, but under a different name and a different rule.

The bus driver, a burly man named Salim, started the engine signalling the bus's departure. The children rushed to the windows to wave goodbye to their parents. Dheeba felt relieved that Salim, a renowned local hero, was taking them on the trip. Salim had driven the bus between Tarshiha and Akka until his retirement; now he only conducted the odd journey here and there for the school or for one of the churches. In the years leading up to the Catastrophe, his had not been the safest of professions. Zionist forces had frequently ambushed Palestinian buses, lynching and assaulting passengers, with the aim of instilling terror in the Palestinian population. It was effective. Once, in the 1940s, Salim had been driving his usual route with a bus full of passengers from Tarshiha.

As he approached the junction at Al-Kabri, he noticed a solitary suitcase at the side of the road, an odd sight that might easily cause people to stop. But Salim recognised something was not right. He shouted at his passengers to get down on the ground. At that very moment, a group of men emerged from the bushes and opened fire on the bus. Salim slammed his foot on the accelerator, driving as fast as the bus could manage. He kept going all the way until they reached Akka. It was only then that the damage was realised: Salim had been badly shot and injured, as had two of the passengers, who in the end didn't survive. More would have been martyred had Salim not been so quick to spot the ambush. The story became a village legend; Salim was hailed as a hero and continued driving the bus route between Tarshiha and Akka after his recovery.

Dheeba watched as the man who had so courageously saved the lives of his passengers started to pull away with the children and their teachers. She exchanged a final wave with Mahmoud, then waited until the bus had turned around the corner and was out of sight. Instinctively she turned in the direction of her house, taking a few steps before pausing. She had some time before she needed to be home. The children would be at school for a few more hours. Dheeba changed direction and started walking towards her mother's house. She considered herself lucky that, after their expulsion, her family had decided to settle in Tarshiha. It meant that she could see them often. Dheeba frequently reminded herself not to take this for granted, especially since, during the Catastrophe, she had come close to being separated from her family forever.

In early 1948, Dheeba had been invited to stay with her aunt and uncle in their village. Aunt Noura had married a rich landowner, Atef Serhan, from Al-Kabri, a village not too far from Tarshiha, towards the coast. The couple lived in one of Al-Kabri's grandest houses, matched in size only by that of Atef's brother, Faris, a well-known nationalist and a member of the Arab Higher Committee. Dheeba admired Noura, who seemed so glamorous with her fancy house and aristocratic in-laws. Noura's daughter, Aliah, was close in age to Dheeba, and they had spent a lot of time together growing up. Upon receipt of the invitation, Dheeba's mother, Hamda, strong-willed and with a soft spot for her eldest daughter, persuaded her husband to allow the visit. The Galilee then was unstable, assailed by ongoing fighting and frequent Zionist ambushes, but by February, Dheeba's father decided conditions were calm enough for his daughter to make the journey ten kilometres south to her aunt's house.

Shortly after Dheeba's arrival, a small band of Zionists attempted to blow up Faris Serhan's house. In retaliation, locals blocked the main coastal road on which the village was strategically situated. The battle for Al-Kabri ensued. The situation escalated in mid-March, when men from the village and from Tarshiha ambushed a Zionist military convoy on its way to a new colony to their east. The villagers surrounded the convoy and opened fire, but they soon ran out of bullets. They sent word to the women in Al-Kabri to call on the nearby Arab Salvation Army unit to join in the fight. Dheeba and Aliah rushed to find the unit to pass on the message. The call was heeded;

back-up arrived quickly, and the Zionist military convoy was soon immobilised. It was a small victory, but jubilations were short-lived. The next day, the village suffered a heavy British bombardment at the Zionists' request. The whole month of April was spent in anticipation of a full-scale retaliatory attack by the Zionists. Al-Kabri was running out of ammunition and supplies. In May, the fall of Akka disheartened the villagers; if a whole city could be defeated, they didn't stand a chance. By then, the people of Al-Kabri were poorly armed, with only fifty or so men and as many rifles. Many others in the village were leaving, fearing a fate of massacre and rape.

On one of those tense evenings spent in wait of potential attack, Dheeba and Aliah eavesdropped on a conversation between the adults, who were debating whether or not to leave. It was then that they heard the story of Yasser Illuti, a fifteen-year-old boy from Al-Shajara. When his village had come under attack, most of the residents fled, leaving only the elderly women behind. Yasser had broken his leg earlier in the year and was unable to walk, and so he too stayed behind in Al-Shajara. The villagers assumed that, as a disabled child, he would not be considered a threat, but even so, the old women decided to hide him in a haystack, just in case. Yasser was soon discovered by the Zionist militias, who were thorough in their ransacking. They pushed him up against a wall and shot him without a second thought. Dheeba and Aliah gasped when they heard how poor Yasser met his end, and that night, Dheeba cried herself to sleep, cradled in her cousin's arms. Yet even worse stories were to come.

In mid-April, news reached Al-Kabri about Deir Yassin, a village near Jerusalem. The Zionist militia known as the Irgun had attacked, killing hundreds of villagers and looting their homes. It seemed that no one was spared. Schoolgirls were brutalised and killed. Old women were molested. They had even heard of a young girl being torn in two. At the time, Dheeba could not comprehend what this meant. When she was older, she understood. It wasn't only in Deir Yassin that rape was being wielded as an instrument of expulsion—and rather successfully so. While the victims were mostly women, sexual violence was being used as a means to control the whole society. Men were fleeing to protect their wives and daughters, as well as the honour of the family. For the victim, being raped meant a lifetime of shame and lessened chances of getting married. This incensed Dheeba. It wasn't enough that women were subjected to unspeakable violence; they also had to suffer social ostracism. She was quickly learning how life for girls was unfair and unrelenting.

The residents of Al-Kabri didn't have long to decide whether to stay or go. A full-scale attack was imminent. In the end, Dheeba's aunt and her husband decided to follow Faris and his family, who had already left for Beirut. Dheeba panicked at the thought of being separated from her own family. There was no way to contact them before leaving. The Zionist forces were taking over the entire Galilee little by little, and messenger routes were not safe. Her aunt promised that they would get word to Dheeba's family as soon as they had arrived safely in Beirut. Besides, Noura told her, it was likely that her parents and siblings would also end up in Lebanon. Dheeba had no choice but to follow. They filled the car with only bare essentials and locked everything else away in the house, carefully hiding their most treasured possessions in case of looters. Atef paid the servants and bade them farewell, and in the morning, they set off on a four-hour drive to Beirut. Noura refused to say goodbye to the house as they left. She turned to Dheeba and Aliah and told them adamantly, 'We'll be back soon.' Dheeba examined her aunt's face for any tinge of doubt or uncertainty, finding no trace of either.

The journey from Al-Kabri to Ras al-Naqoura, the crossing point to Lebanon, was emotionally painful. The roads were crammed with cars, trucks and people. Those who didn't own cars could only take what they could bear on their backs. Dheeba watched out of the car window as women carrying babies abandoned their possessions along the way. She felt both guilty and relieved to be making the journey in Atef's car. The Serhans were among the privileged few Palestinian refugees whose financial circumstances afforded them a good living after their displacement. This relative fortune naturally extended to Dheeba, who was under the family's care and protection. On reaching Beirut, they drove straight to an apartment that Atef had rented not far from the infamous Hamra Street. The quarters were modest, but enough for them all to live comfortably together. Dheeba felt grateful to enjoy such grandeur, yet also somewhat uneasy. After all, she had grown up in a simple, two-room house with neither electricity nor water.

Not long after their arrival in Lebanon, the family discovered that many of those who had remained in Al-Kabri were executed. Others were interrogated as to the whereabouts of Faris Serhan, before being expelled. Noura desperately tried to find out the fate of her friends and family members. There was barely any news. However, word reached her that the Zionists had smashed open the doors of their house and ransacked it. Some days, Noura seethed with rage, screaming at the barbarity of the Zionists. Other days, she broke down sobbing. During this time, Dheeba and Aliah sought solace and comfort in each other. Aliah was familiar with Beirut from previous trips, and so she could guide her cousin through her new surroundings.

Dheeba thought of Beirut as the more chic sister of Haifa. The two cities shared the sticky, Mediterranean humidity of air and sea crashing against a mountainous backdrop. Their resemblance made competition inevitable, but there was a popular recognition that Beirut had a flare that Haifa lacked. This was partly due to Lebanon's declaration of independence from the French mandate in 1943. Beirut, in particular, also enjoyed a reputation as an exotic Eastern hotspot for European tourists; the city was full of clubs and hotels and catered to a young, wealthy and cosmopolitan crowd. Haifa never received that same attention. But despite its glamour, Beirut was not impervious to what was happening in its neighbourhood. The Palestinian Catastrophe had irrevocably changed Lebanon's character. At least a hundred thousand Palestinian refugees had crossed over the border seeking safety and shelter. This, along with the establishment of a hard and hostile border between Lebanon and Palestine, inevitably changed the country.

Soon after they settled in, Atef suggested that Dheeba take up work at his friend's clothing factory, which employed young refugee women from Palestine. He explained that it would give her an income of her own and a more structured daily routine. Dheeba, relishing the prospect of independence after so long under the kind but watchful eye of Noura, jumped at the opportunity. At the factory, she found herself working amongst other young women in similar circumstances of exile. She especially warmed to a woman called Nizar, a name more commonly given to boys than to girls. In keeping with her unconventional name, Nizar had a tendency to break the rules. She spoke honestly, without caring what others thought of her, and had a sharp sense of humour that entertained everyone throughout the long hours of sewing and cutting cloth. The work itself was not very strenuous, especially compared to what Dheeba was used to. The women would have the radio on in the background during their shifts. Month by month, they listened as more Palestinian villages, towns and cities fell to the Zionist forces. Sometimes, when the news became overwhelming, Nizar would get up and switch over to a music station. No one objected. They needed the relief.

The Zionists declared their new state on the fourteenth of May, not long after Dheeba and the Serhan family had reached Beirut. The announcement was made in the Jewish city of Tel Aviv, situated to the north of Yaffa. They heard on the radio that crowds of new Jewish immigrants had gathered to celebrate the creation of 'Israel'. At this point, quite suddenly and unceremoniously, the British High Commissioner for Palestine left the country with his staff. According to the mandate, the British were to hand over authority and assets to a governing local entity. But they didn't. Their exit, while officially ending British rule in Palestine, was also an open invitation for the Zionists to take over the whole country.

The declaration provoked a strong reaction from the Arab states. From Beirut, Dheeba watched as the next day, armed forces and volunteers from Egypt, Jordan, Lebanon, Iraq and Syria marched into Palestine to fight the Zionists. Everyone assumed that the Arabs—being larger in number and knowing the terrain better—would win. Dheeba was sceptical. She didn't believe they were truly interested in liberating Palestine; it seemed to her that their stakes in protecting the Holy Land were political. Indeed, the bitterest fighting took place in Jerusalem and its surroundings. The Arabs took control of the Old City, but the Zionists held on to the affluent Palestinian neighbourhoods in West Jerusalem, like Qatamon and Talbiya, which Dheeba knew were famed for their beautiful tree-lined avenues and extravagant villas. Then, rather abruptly, having secured its hold over the West Bank, Jordan paused its advance. The British called for a ceasefire. Less than two weeks after their arrival, many of the Arab armies agreed and put down their weapons. Meanwhile, there were reports that the Zionists were continuing to import arms from countries in Eastern Europe.

As news from Palestine grew ever darker, Dheeba was building a new life for herself in Beirut. She began spending more time outside of work with Aliah and her new friends. Coming to terms with the possibility of her permanent exile in Lebanon, she explored the city with fervour, frequenting the local shops, cafes and cinemas. On Fridays, Atef drove them all down to the Corniche—Beirut's seaside promenade—along which they would stroll for hours. It seemed to be popular among Palestinians, so much so that they were only ever able to walk for a few minutes before having to stop and greet friends and acquaintances. These conversations were predominately about flight and exile; they swapped stories and shared the latest news, transforming the Corniche into a living, breathing radio. For Dheeba, exile was made easier with so many Palestinians around her, yet their numbers broke her heart.

Dheeba's life continued like this for the rest of the year. She oscillated between temporary contentedness, when she pushed her exile to the back of her mind, and sorrowful dejection, as she held on to a wish to return home. The Serhans, however, did not entertain any such hopes. Their family's political reputation meant that returning was out of the question. They would certainly be arrested, possibly even executed, if they tried. One day in October, Dheeba caught Noura crying in her husband's arms in the living room. 'Rahat Falasteen,' she repeated. 'Palestine is gone.' Atef didn't reply. Staring at the floor, he rocked her back and forth. Dheeba retreated out of the room. She felt embarrassed for having stumbled upon such a private moment. As she made her way down the corridor, she heard the crackle of the radio and a news broadcast. The Zionists had occupied the Negev—the Naqab—and were on the cusp of taking over the Galilee. This was the final assault in the occupation of Palestine.

By early 1949, the Arab countries had begun to draw up armistice lines with the new Israeli state. It encompassed more than three quarters of Palestine, with only the West Bank and Gaza remaining in Arab hands. Closely observing the situation, Atef came to Dheeba with a surprising ultimatum. The International Red Cross was assisting the reunification of family members—in some cases. The Zionist regime was refusing the applications of men and older boys, considering them to be potential militants, but the Red Cross had persuaded them to allow the reunification of girls and women. Atef had a contact within the organisation and was willing to make a case for Dheeba. He stressed that this would likely be her one and only chance to go back to Palestine.

Although Dheeba's family had also initially fled to Lebanon, they had managed to make their way back to Palestine a few months later. Dheeba hadn't even seen them during their short time in exile. She missed them desperately. Without deliberating, Dheeba pleaded with Atef to make the case for her. He did so convincingly, and her application was quickly accepted, suddenly leaving her with only a few days more in Beirut, the city that had been her home for so many months. As she prepared to say goodbye to her relatives and new friends, she knew the hardest person to leave would be Aliah. Ever since

Dheeba's arrival in Al-Kabri, the pair had formed a strong bond—that of sisters rather than cousins. On the day of her departure, Aliah wiped the tears from Dheeba's face, promising to see her soon. The family accompanied her to the Red Cross office, where a bus waited that would take her back to Palestine through the Ras al-Naqoura crossing. That was the last time she ever saw Aliah and her family.

Dheeba sighed at the memory. Her life would have been so vastly different had she stayed in Beirut. She was lucky to have made it back, to have been reunited with her family, to have returned to Palestinian soil. She carried on walking towards her parents' house, reaching the steep hill that led there. Along with many of her siblings, Dheeba's parents lived in the upper part of the village. Over time and with their expanding family, they had formed their own neighbourhood. As newcomers without marriage links to the village, Dheeba's parents were considered outsiders by some, who never let them forget that they were refugees. Dheeba herself was still referred to as Al-Badawiya—the Bedouin—though she was well integrated into Tarshiha as the wife of a Tarshihani. Sadly, prejudices were abundant and rife across Palestine, whether against the Bedouin, fallaheen, refugees or others. Dheeba found it troubling that a people who had suffered so much oppression could be guilty of turning against each other.

Still, she was grateful that at least her family were internal refugees and that they hadn't been exiled beyond the border. Sheer luck featured in the story of nearly every Palestinian who had survived the Catastrophe and remained in Palestine. Her family had returned just in time to be counted in the new state's census. It was thanks to her mother, who had stubbornly insisted on their return. Her father had not wanted to risk it, but her mother's determination and courage had prevailed. Others had not been so fortunate. Countless people had attempted that same return. Many were men who had gone back to Palestine to check if it was safe, in the hope of sending for their wives and children later. Thousands were shot and killed, others caught, arrested and later dumped in the Jordanian-controlled West Bank.

On returning to Palestine, Dheeba had spent the first few months in a state of shock. The landscape had already significantly changed. A new country had violently been planted on top of her land. The sheer scale of the destruction was disorientating. Dheeba would soon learn that the Zionists had obliterated hundreds of Palestinian villages. Towns and villages she had once known intimately now stood ruined and empty. Others had been completely taken over by Jewish settlers, their original inhabitants exiled. The number of Jewish immigrants had nearly doubled. To accommodate them, the regime was also building rapidly. There were new roads leading to new settlements and new signs in Hebrew. Arabic had been wiped from everything. Even the names of former Palestinian villages—names that had evolved and been passed down over centuries—had now been Hebraised. Al-Zeeb became Akhziv, Al-Basa became Betset, and Ras al-Naqoura became Rosh Hanikra. It was not enough that these places were erased physically; they had to be erased from memory. But such a task would pose a challenge for the new state, for Palestinians' ingrained culture of oral transmission meant they had collectively memorised their history and landscape. Dheeba too had a deeply detailed cognitive map of Palestine, featuring places she hadn't even visited but that she knew thoroughly from stories.

In those early years, the Israeli army had confined the surviving Palestinians in their villages and urban ghettoes. Night curfews were a standard feature of everyday life, as were deliberate electricity cuts. In a sick twist of events, the Israeli government leased back the land they had stolen to the original owners so that they could farm and herd their animals. Even then, the Palestinians were strictly forbidden from building on this land and had to apply for permits for every aspect of their daily lives, from farming to seeking medical treatment. Of course, in this repressive environment, permit violations were common. All around her, Dheeba saw people desperate to harvest their crops and graze their animals. A denied or expired permit would simply lead them to do it anyway and face the consequences. These were sometimes brutal. The Zionists had set up makeshift military tribunals to deal with infractions. People were given fines, and many were forced to choose incarceration for lack of means to pay. Dheeba saw young children being carted off for interrogation, where they would be threatened with violence unless they provided information about their family members. Humiliations were routine for those who did not comply with the Zionists' orders. The authorities would viciously abuse the people, yet the Zionist settlers could be just as bad, or even worse. Lynch mobs searched for Palestinians to beat up, and being spat at was common.

The situation was truly horrible and confounding. Dheeba felt homesick—not for a place, but rather for a time. A time before everything had changed.

Dheeba paused halfway up the hill to catch her breath. Putting her hand on her hip, she smiled as several people passed and greeted her as Um Mahmoud, mother of Mahmoud. It was a steep climb to her parents' house, and her calves were aching from working in the fields. She usually had some kind of muscle pain or another. It was a hard life being the wife of a fallah. If you wanted to eat, you had to work, and the women worked as hard as the men. Laziness was not tolerated. When the children were too young for school, Dheeba would bring them along to the fields with their cots and place them beside her as she worked. During the tobacco harvest, all able hands in the family and extended family were expected to participate. They woke up early and headed to the crop, where they picked and gathered the tobacco, stopping briefly for breakfast before stringing up the tobacco leaves. It was the same rhythm for the olive harvest in the late autumn, and it was back-breaking work. While the men were up in the trees beating the branches to release their fruits, the women were bent over sorting the olives from the debris. Once the olives had been harvested, they were divided into those for pickling and those for soap and olive oil. The produce was shared amongst the extended Hawari family and would just about last them until the next harvest. This was the life that Dheeba had chosen.

It was two years after her return from Lebanon that Dheeba had met Kamel. He was one of her father's business acquaintances and sometimes passed by their home. Whenever that happened, Dheeba and her sisters made sure to be around the house. Despite his stern face, Kamel was young and handsome. Dheeba noticed his kind eyes. She liked him. They had talked a few times, and she was confident that he liked her too. Sure enough, one day, Dheeba's father told her that Kamel had expressed his interest in marrying her. After a few chaperoned meetings, Dheeba agreed. The wedding was quickly arranged. There was no point in dragging out an engagement; life was too short. After all the turmoil and precariousness of the past years, marriage signified a completely new and stable life for Dheeba. She would move out from her parents' house to live with her husband, embracing the working lifestyle of a fallah's wife and having a family. Thus, in many ways, marriage marked the beginning of adulthood. Dheeba was excited about this, and even more so about the wedding. Through her father's contacts, they were able to smuggle in cloth and lace from Beirut. When the materials arrived, she squeezed them tightly in her hands, savouring the renewed connection with her beloved city. She took the cloth and lace to Dar al-Najameh, a renowned dressmaker in Akka. There, she placed instructions for a simple yet elegant dress.

The night before the wedding, Dheeba's sisters accompanied her to Tarshiha—her new adoptive village. They stayed up late eating sweets, drinking tea and talking at length about what her new life would be like. As the eldest daughter, Dheeba would be the first amongst them to get married. She felt grown up with her new title as a bride. Giggling, her sisters shared stories that they had heard about married life, including about what happened on the wedding night. Physical intimacy of that kind was not experienced before marriage. Dheeba felt her cheeks blush with embarrassment, but her sisters paid no attention in their excitement. She also felt a tinge of apprehension knowing that Kamel had been married before and that he surely had expectations. She wondered if she could live up to them. She had no doubt that she would love him, but would he love her as much? Pushing these thoughts aside, she allowed her sisters' chatter to distract her.

The next morning, Dheeba's sisters helped her put on her dress from Beirut. They pinned back her curly hair and smoothed it down with oil, dabbed rouge on her cheeks and lips and lined her eyes with kohl. The wedding was a traditional affair, during which the two families came together to celebrate their union. Dheeba greeted hundreds of guests, most of whom she didn't know. Mountains of food were prepared, yet, as was usual, the bride and groom barely ate a bite. Nor did they manage to talk to each other, but amidst the chaos, they sometimes caught each other's eye or briefly brushed the other's hand. In these special moments of shared intimacy, Dheeba's apprehensions of the previous night began to melt away and she allowed herself to be happy. She was leaving her parents, her siblings and her home, but she would now begin building a new life with Kamel.

It was another stroke of luck that she did not end up very far from her family. After pausing a few minutes to catch her breath, Dheeba continued up the hill. She finally reached her parents' garden, catching sight of the inked shapes on her hands as she pushed opened the gate. Tattooing was a common practice for Bedouin women. As girls, Dheeba and her sisters had collected thistle needles and filled them with ink, taking turns to draw different patterns on each other. Unfortunately, they were not particularly skilled, and many of the shapes were neither intricate nor beautiful. Dheeba liked them even so. Her mother, however, had been furious. She lamented the ruin of her daughter's beautiful skin. 'Why didn't you let me do it?' she scolded. But the damage was already done; the ink was etched into her skin forever. By contrast, her mother's anger dissipated soon enough.

As the eldest daughter among many children, Dheeba was close to her mother. Their relationship had developed into a friendship, for as Dheeba grew older, she had begun to live more of her mother's experiences. Their shared womanhood brought them together, especially when they both fell pregnant at the same time. Now, standing in her mother's garden, Dheeba caught a glimpse of her through the window. She smiled to herself and knocked on the front door.

HAMDA

As the morning sunshine flooded into her kitchen, Hamda took a deep breath, inhaling the mountainous air. The morning had been a flustered one. Her youngest son, Nawaf, had left with his classmates on a trip south to the areas newly occupied by the Zionists. Hamda had awoken early to prepare a bundle of food for him to take on the journey. While carefully wrapping date-filled biscuits and pieces of sliced fruit, she had thought of all the places Nawaf would visit—places that she herself had never been. The capital, Jerusalem, was further away than both Beirut and Damascus. She had never needed to go, and the opportunity had never arisen. She had seen photographs in newspapers and heard stories from relatives who had travelled; they talked with awe about the great walls of Jerusalem and the old souqs of Nablus. Yet for Hamda, these bustling cities held little appeal, seeming to her to be claustrophobic and dirty. Rural life was all that she had ever known and all that she loved.

Hamda was born to a Bedouin tribe known as Arab al-Samniya in northern Palestine at the turn of the century, when the land was occupied by the Ottomans. When she was just six years old, she was sent to the coastal village of Al-Bassa to go to school, an unusual enterprise for Bedouin girls. Alas, it was short-lived;

only a few years after her enrolment, her father passed away, meaning that there was no one to pay for her education. In an instant, Hamda's life was flipped upside down. She was withdrawn from school and sent to live at her grandparents' house, where she was thrust prematurely into adulthood and had to contribute to the family's livelihood. It seemed that everyone around her was unsympathetic to the sudden loss of her father, her schooling and her childhood. 'Such is life,' they told her, 'unfair and full of unwanted surprises.' Hamda tried to retain what little she had learned in school, but unfortunately, all she could hold on to was how to write her name in Arabic.

Things around Hamda were also changing. Although their lands remained under Ottoman rule, Constantinople's control was waning, and the people could sense that the empire was coming to an end. At the same time, Palestine was becoming more independent and more nationalist by the day. The famine of 1915 had ravaged the region, leaving over half a million dead. People were hungry and poor, and it was making them angry. Hamda often saw the men excitedly distributing newspapers and overheard their enthusiastic and sometimes heated conversations about an independent Palestine. Meanwhile, their way of life was being drastically transformed. The railway had been expanded to cover the whole Palestinian coastline and beyond. Travel between cities and around the region was becoming faster, cheaper and more convenient. To Hamda, it felt like they were on the brink of something significant.

Sure enough, when Hamda was about fifteen years old, the Ottomans were driven out of Palestine by the British. Initial excitement among Palestinians about the possibility for self-rule was quickly smothered with the onset of the British mandate. Promises made to the Arab peoples and to Sharif Hussein, the self-declared King of the Arabs, were quickly forgotten. The changes in Palestine were dramatic. Ottoman life was all that Hamda had ever known; it was all that twenty generations of her people had known. Now, one foreign ruler had been replaced by another. But this time, they looked and sounded even less like her.

It was around this time that Hamda married Hamoud, a Bedouin man a few years older than her and from the same tribe. The marriage was arranged by their families, and it proved to be a suitable match. Hamoud was tall and slender and could provide well for Hamda. They moved into their own beit sha'ar—goat-hair tent—and soon after celebrated the arrival of their first child. But Hamda's second and third pregnancies were hard on her, the labours even worse, and she lost her next two children during childbirth. Fearful that her fourth child, a beautiful baby girl, would also meet an early death, Hamda immediately named her Dheeba, 'she-wolf', to ward away the evil eye. The totem worked. Dheeba—and all of the children who came after her—survived the perils of early life that had taken her two elder siblings. All in all, Hamda gave birth to six daughters and four sons over a span of three decades; like so many women, including Dheeba after her, she would see her life dictated by the rhythms of childbearing. Dheeba was the baby who broke the spell, and so throughout her life, Hamda always maintained a soft spot for her eldest daughter, the she-wolf.

The British took control of most aspects of life in Palestine, ruling with a complete and unwavering sense of entitlement. They acted as if they knew the land better than the Palestinians, whom they disdained as ignoble and uncivilised. Hamda's few encounters with British soldiers proved as much. They looked at her with pity, sometimes even sneering at her. She didn't understand English, but she could guess the meaning of the jokes made at her expense. Worse still, the soldiers frequently stopped Hamoud and their sons for tafteesh—frisking—making them stand with their hands on their heads while aggressively patting them down. It was a routine humiliation.

What bewildered Hamda the most was that the British lived in Palestine as though they were still at home. They built infrastructure and architecture that was totally alien to the land, as if trying to replicate Britain in the Middle East. So comfortable were they in their own superiority that they brought their bizarre customs with them even when these were starkly out of place. One day, while foraging for wild asparagus in the mountains, Hamda heard shouts and the sounds of galloping horses. A group of men on horseback appeared, unmistakably British in their attire of formal tailored coats, beige trousers and long boots. They came to a halt not far from her, stopping to drink water. Then, one of the men blew a horn, and off they rode. Hamda later learned that they had been hunting a jackal—not to eat, but for the fun of the chase. This was apparently considered a sport in Britain, and it had surreally been transplanted to the vast, rolling hills of the Galilee.

As well as setting up their own administrative rule, the British established various local committees, institutions and police forces, into which they recruited Palestinians. At the outbreak of World War Two, thousands of Palestinians volunteered to serve in the British army. Some remained convinced that the British were preparing them for independent rule. It was a short-lived hope. As time wore on, it became increasingly clear that the British were providing unparalleled support to the Zionist settlement of Palestine, awarding settlers high positions in their administration. Hamoud was infuriated by the deceit. Hamda, on the other hand, expected nothing less.

In 1936, during the Great Revolt, an uprising against the British colonial forces in Palestine, Hamoud took up arms and became part of the resistance. As a skilled marksman, he was placed in charge of not only smuggling weapons but also guerrilla actions in the north. One operation involved targeting one of the new British police stations that were popping up all across Palestine in response to the uprising, functioning as mini forts to detain, interrogate and torture the local populations. In Al-Suwaneh, Hamoud and his fellow guerrilla fighters burned the police station to the ground; no sooner was it rebuilt than they burned it down once again.

The guerrillas were also involved in ambushes against British military convoys. This frightened Hamda the most. It was dangerous work, particularly as they were always outnumbered and outgunned. In one notorious ambush, Hamoud had barely survived. He and his fellow guerrillas had organised an attack on a convoy escorting Zionist leaders to a colony near the village of Hanoota. On trusted intelligence, the guerrillas launched their attack near Al-Bassa, driving one of the convoy's cars into a ditch. A gun battle ensued, and just as it looked like the guerrillas might win, the convoy radioed for military support. Hamoud and his comrades were no match for the British bomber planes that heeded the call. Those who survived were hunted down and arrested. Hamoud was taken to Akka Prison, where he narrowly escaped the death penalty, thanks to the intervention of Faris Serhan, his sister Noura's husband's brother, who had connections within the British administration. Some years before, Mohammed Jamjoum, Ata Alzeer and Fouad Hijazi had been hanged in the very same prison for taking part in the Buraq Revolt in Jerusalem. Theirs became a heroic tale of martyrdom, but also a forewarning of the ruthlessness of the British forces, and it was turned into a popular folk song. Hamda always shuddered when she heard this song. It reminded her that Hamoud had nearly met the same fate.

Life during this time was cruel, and efforts to crush any form of resistance were severe. There were frequent raids on Palestinian villages and homes by British soldiers, sometimes supported by Zionist militias. A common tactic was to line up all of the village's men and shoot dead every eighth one until someone revealed the whereabouts of hidden weapons. Often, there were no weapons to give up, and the soldiers knew as much. This reign of terror eventually succeeded in crushing the revolt. Meanwhile, the number of Zionist settlers was growing at an alarming rate. They established a workforce and an economy that were entirely separate to those of the Arabs. Hamda saw these developments with her own eyes whenever she visited neighbouring towns and villages.

Throughout this period, the Arab al-Samniyeh tribe started to abandon their traditional tent dwellings and began building houses in Jalil, their village. In 1942, Hamoud followed suit; recruiting a builder from Damascus, he had a house made for Hamda and his children on their land, nestled at the foot of one of the mountains bordering Lebanon. It was a simple stone house, rectangular in shape, with large, arched windows and three spacious rooms for entertaining and sleeping. Citrus and pomegranate trees were planted around the dwelling, along with a carob tree at its entrance to provide shade in the summer months. Despite its simplicity, Hamda was immensely proud of her new home.

The memory of her stone house brought tears to Hamda's eyes. She glanced around her current home with sadness. They had lived in this house in Tarshiha for nearly ten years. It too was simple, but it neither was beautiful nor evoked a sense of pride. Indeed, it had really belonged to another family, one that had been exiled during the Catastrophe. When Hamda's family had moved to Tarshiha, they had been permitted to rent this house from the state. Hamda felt it was a particularly cruel irony that they had been removed from their home only to be told to resettle in that of another displaced family. Worse than that, they had to pay rent to the very people who had forced them out. In an effort to counter the injustice of it all, Hamda told her children that when the original owners of the house returned, they would give it up. 'We're caretakers of this house,' she would reiterate. For this reason, Hamda always made sure that the house was impeccably tidy. She had packed up the belongings that were not theirs and placed them in storage above the kitchen, keeping them safe until the owners returned. Tending to the garden, she planted vegetables and fragrant herbs close to the house and repaired the garden wall to prevent wild animals from eating them. She then introduced a variety of trees for shade and privacy. But she couldn't bring herself to plant a carob tree. She already had one, and it was waiting for her.

All through, she made sure that she never got too comfortable or felt too at home. It was only temporary, after all, she would remind herself. But temporary had turned into more than a decade. The owners of the house had not returned, and neither had Hamda's family returned to their home. She looked over to where her husband was resting. He had been up and about this morning even before she had risen to prepare for Nawaf's trip. Hamoud's usual routine involved an early start. He tended to the animals and a small plot of land not far from their house. On returning home, he would spend much of the remainder of the day napping. In the beginning, he had tried to maintain a semblance of their past life, but he couldn't keep up the illusion. He had become a different man since the Catastrophe and their expulsion. It was as though he had taken on the burden of the loss physically. His shoulders were often hunched, making him appear shorter. He seemed to complain of more ailments than before. And even though he had always been a man of few words, he now barely spoke. Hamda's gaze lingered on her husband as she remembered the person he had once been. Had she also changed? She wasn't sure. She was certainly angrier, but she also felt stronger. Traumatic events and experiences could do that—they could harden you, but they could also break you. She was worried that Hamoud would never be able to climb his way out of the pit of devastation into which he had been plunged. She took solace in the fact that it wasn't only them, that they had all changed in some way. After all, they had been through so much, so quickly.

Palestinians began fleeing their homes, towns and cities long before the Zionist state declared its independence in the early summer of 1948. The violence had already begun the year before, and the many stories of massacres and lootings gave momentum to the flight. People lived in a constant state of anxiety and terror, awaiting news from the south of Zionist militia advances and gains. The Arab al-Samniyeh had discussed their defences and what to do in the event of an invasion of their lands. They would only be capable of holding out for so long and would have to go into hiding in the mountains until the attack was over.

During what seemed like a brief lull in the fighting, Dheeba had pleaded with her mother to let her go and stay with her aunt Noura, who lived in Al-Kabri, a village not too far away. Their life had become monotonous, and they hadn't seen family for months. Besides, the road to Al-Kabri was still relatively free of militias, and once she arrived, Dheeba would be safe under the protection of Noura's husband's family, the Serhans. Hamda had succumbed and asked Hamoud to let their daughter travel. Yet, from the moment Dheeba left, Hamda regretted her decision, and an unshakeable sense of impending doom overcame her. Her intuition was right. A few weeks after Dheeba departed, the fight came to Al-Kabri. The villagers put up an intense resistance, angering the Zionist leaders. Hamoud sent word to Noura that she and her family should leave and send Dheeba back home, but it soon became clear that the roads were no longer safe. Eventually, just before the new state's declaration of independence, Noura's family was forced to flee to Lebanon, along with Dheeba. Hamda's concern for her eldest daughter was soon overshadowed by fear for herself, Hamoud and the rest of their children. The Zionist forces continued to attack the northern coastal plains around Akka, advancing closer and closer to the stone house. Each day, Hamda and Hamoud were inundated with requests for water or food by people fleeing to the border. They gave them what little they had. Hamoud even presented one man with a pair of shoes upon seeing that his were battered. 'God knows how long he'd been walking, but it must have been far, because the soles were completely worn through!' he recounted to Hamda. Seeing people pass by in droves took its toll on Hamoud. He grew increasingly concerned and agitated. One morning, he brought up the notion of leaving. Hamda jerked her head towards him and snapped, 'If you want to leave, you can do so on your own.'

Word soon reached them that Dheeba had arrived safely in Beirut. By then, many of the Arab al-Samniyeh were also fleeing. Testimonies of the violence in the south were chilling. The Zionists were under instructions to clear the entire coast of Palestinian inhabitants, and they did so with great efficiency. In the north, out of sixty-five villages, only two survived the Catastrophe. Tantura, a small Palestinian fishing village south of Haifa, was one of many that did not. Dheeba had not known anything of Tantura before the Catastrophe. Like so many villages, it became synonymous with the tragedy that befell it. A common Zionist tactic was to surround villages on three sides, leaving one side open to funnel fleeing villagers either north to Lebanon or east to Syria and Jordan. In Tantura, however, they surrounded the village from the land and the sea, leaving no route for escape. After a very brief fight, the villagers forfeited, raising their white kuffiyehs over their heads. Hopeless as it was to fend off the attack, they thought that a surrender would spare them more deaths. They were wrong. The Zionist militia began vicious killing sprees, before gathering the remaining population on the beach. Groups of men were lined up against a wall and shot in the back of their heads. Although women were mostly spared execution, many were subjected to horrific sexual violence. Some were so brutally raped that they were sent to a hospital in Nablus for treatment. Several hundred villagers were massacred. The survivors were held in the village for several days before being transferred. They slept amongst the rubble and the bodies of their dead fathers, uncles, brothers and sons, whom they were not permitted to bury. Instead, the Zionist militia brought men from a nearby village to inter the dead in a mass grave. It was said that after a week, a mound began to form above the ground because there were so many corpses inflating beneath the soil.

This particular story played on Hamoud's mind as he pondered whether to leave. Gently resting his hand on his wife's shoulder, he raised the issue again a few days later. 'It won't be for long. Just until the fighting stops.' He didn't want to frighten her too and so spared her the story of the Tantura massacres. But Hamda had already heard. She had eyes and ears everywhere, and she could see the fear in Hamoud's eyes as he spoke. She thought of her children, and of Dheeba in Beirut. Her hand went to stroke her belly; she was bringing another into the world very soon. This time, she didn't argue with him.

They packed up a few possessions, along with the bare essentials for the journey—food and warm clothing. Even though it was summer, the mountains could get cold at night, and they didn't know how long they would be on the road. They had to be prepared for the worst. Amongst the few belongings that Hamda took with them was the gold Hamoud had given her on their wedding. It wasn't much, but it held sentimental value. Hamda would distribute it between her girls when they each got married. She wrapped the pieces in cloth and placed them in a pouch, which she tucked away under her bosom. After taking one last look around the stone house, they boarded it up, making sure to lock and bolt the door before setting off.

The journey would not be easy. They had five children of varying ages, including a baby, and Hamda was heavily pregnant. At first, they hid in the mountains near their home, living in a beit sha'ar. But as the Zionist forces progressed, they were pushed further north towards Lebanon. They continued on to Huwara, an area on the border with Lebanon. It was here that Hamda went into labour on the side of the road. With no knowledge of midwifery, Hamoud ran in search of help, returning quickly with a woman from the nearby village. Together they tried to make Hamda as comfortable as possible under a makeshift shelter. The delivery was mercifully quick, and miraculously, after a few hours, baby Ahmad was born.

Just a few days after the birth, they decided to keep on walking. Hamda was at near collapse from exhaustion by the time they crossed into Lebanon. They reached a Shi'a village called Shihin, where Hamoud decided to stop and put down a beit sha'ar. The villagers were friendly and welcoming, having been receiving refugees from Palestine for months. Some time after, they moved into a rented house. It took some convincing. Hamda felt like moving into a house was more permanent. She didn't want to set up a home anywhere but in her stone house at the foot of the mountain. It was 'for the sake of the children,' as Hamoud put it, that she eventually relented.

News trickled in from Palestine every day. The war came to a head in the autumn when the battle for the Galilee intensified. From Shihin, they could hear the bombs fall on their friends and neighbours. It was excruciating. Towards the end of the year, the bombing stopped and the land fell quiet. The war was drawing to an end. In the south, the Egyptians held on to Gaza. Meanwhile the Jordanian army had cemented its position on the West Bank of the River Jordan. Armistice lines were drawn up, signalling a ceasefire between the Arab countries and the new Zionist state. People were still fleeing their homes, and many more were being expelled. The new state was meting out retribution and hunting down anyone who had taken part in the resistance. Anyone trying to return, whether by boat or by foot, was gunned down. Hamoud was firm that they would not attempt to go back until he could guarantee their safety. Hamda, on the other hand, was anxious to go home. They had escaped the worst of the fighting, and now they had to make sure that their lands and house were not stolen from them. In her gut, Hamda knew that every day they stayed in Lebanon only made their return more unlikely. The Zionists were not the British. She had seen how they were buying thousands of dunams from absentee landlords, kicking tenants off land they had farmed for centuries, and that they were building up their own economy and excluding Palestinians from it. The Zionists were planning to stay. And with hundreds of thousands of Palestinians in exile, the land was unprotected. They could simply take it all.

It was several months after their arrival in Shihin that Hamda started to plot their return. Hamoud spent most of the day out of the house looking for odd jobs to support the family. This gave Hamda plenty of time to begin hatching her plan. She realised that Hamoud would only return if he were forced to do so. She would have to lie to her husband. Hamda set her scheme in motion in late November, packing up the family's things slowly so as not to attract attention. She got in contact with a Bedouin camel driver who was willing to take her to the border. As discreetly as possible, she took money from Hamoud's purse to pay him, praying that her husband wouldn't notice it missing.

The morning of their departure arrived. Hamda was the only one who knew they were leaving. She rushed into the house in a feigned fluster, telling Hamoud that a man passing through the village had a message for him: someone from the Serhan family was eager to meet with him about a job prospect and would be waiting for him in the coastal city of Sour. Eager to find work, Hamoud quickly set off. As soon as he was gone, Hamda hurriedly packed up their remaining belongings and gathered all the children together, explaining that they were going home and that their father would soon join them. Loading up their possessions onto the camel, Hamda glanced in the direction of the main road, which Hamoud had disappeared down only a short while before. She prayed that her plan would work and that he would follow them home.

As they made their way towards the border, the seriousness of what she had done began to dawn on her. Up until now, she had been so determined to reach Palestine that she hadn't dwelled on all the things that could go wrong. What if Hamoud didn't follow them? What if he were caught? Or if they were caught? These were not remote possibilities, no less likely, in fact, than that her plan would succeed. The sudden torrent of anxieties was cut short by the camel driver, who began to complain that the route was becoming more dangerous. Hamda felt sorry; even though he was getting paid, she knew he was taking a great risk for them. But they couldn't stop now. She slipped the man a few extra coins, and, begrudgingly, he carried on.

They reached a spot on the border where, rumour had it, it was easy to cross. Hamda looked at her children and at their belongings packed on the camels. Crossing with their load would be arduous and slow, increasing their chances of being detected by Zionist soldiers. She pleaded with the camel driver to take them just a little further. Whether out of guilt or exasperation, he continued with them across the border into Palestine, until they reached a mountain near the village of Arab al-Aramshe. Here the driver hastily left them, wishing them God's protection for the rest of their journey. Hamda looked towards the valley below. They were so close. In a sheltered spot, she set up a beit sha'ar facing in the direction of their stone house. Her children, confused and exhausted, soon fell asleep. Outside, Hamda sat down on a flat stone and waited, on what would be one of the longest nights of her life.

Back in Lebanon, Hamoud had returned to Shihin, frustrated that the man from the Serhan family was nowhere to be found. In fact, no one in Sour had even heard of the man. Wearily, he walked back to the house he had rented, but upon entering he found it empty— not only of his wife and children, but also of most of their belongings. In panic, Hamoud ran to the nearest neighbour to ask what had happened. He was told that his family had returned to Palestine with a camel herder. Fear rushed over him; he felt his heart stop a moment before suddenly springing back into action. 'They can't have got far,' he thought, as he rushed to find someone in the village with a steed. Before long, he was racing on horseback towards the border with one of the villagers. At the same crossing point that Hamda had used, they parted ways, and Hamoud travelled the remaining distance by foot, dodging the Zionist patrols as he went. Hamoud was a man of fighting age; no soldier would think twice about shooting him dead. On the road, he passed dozens of young men travelling in the opposite direction towards Lebanon. They looked like fighters, and all wore expressions of exhaustion and humiliation. None greeted him as they passed. Hamoud didn't blame them; not only were they defeated and retreating, but collaborators were also rife. He fixed his gaze on the road ahead and concentrated on his mission to find his wife and family. For lack of any information as to where they had gone, he made his way in the direction of the stone house.

After several hours, Hamoud came upon the beit sha'ar. Whether it was luck or divine intervention, he wasn't sure. He found Hamda sitting on a stone nearby and stirring a pot of tea. She looked up at him and offered a relieved smile. Angry and exhausted, Hamoud had no words. He sat down beside her and accepted a cup of tea.

Recalling that reconciliatory brew, Hamda smiled to herself. She knew that she was stubborn and that her conviction was strong. Hamoud always grumbled about this, but if it weren't for her, they would most likely now be living in a refugee camp in Lebanon. At least here, although not in their home, they were in their country. She filled up a pot with water and went outside to gather some herbs. After deliberating a few moments, she settled on maramia—sage—which would help to calm Hamoud's stomach. No doubt the pains that he complained of came from the tobacco he insisted on chewing, she thought to herself. After bringing the water to boil, she stewed the tea and sage leaves for a few minutes before pouring the infusion into glasses, placing one beside her husband, who was resting on some cushions on the floor. From the kitchen, she grabbed a box that was full to the brim with akkoub—gundelia thistle—and sat down on the doorstep. A neighbour had foraged the plant near Jenin and had kindly gifted some to her. It was hard to come by, because it grew in the rocky parts of the mountains that were difficult to reach. As such, akkoub was considered a delicacy, but its preparation was tiresome. The thistles had to be cut away carefully to reveal the plant's head. The head in turn was covered in smaller spikes, which had to be removed with meticulous precision to avoid shedding the meat of the plant. Hamda set to work, scissors in one hand and prickly plant in the other.

During the family's brief flight to Lebanon, the stone house had been occupied by Zionist forces, who had stationed the local army commander himself inside. After a few months living in the beit sha'ar on the mountain looking down on their house, Hamoud went to see some Polish Jewish acquaintances in Elon, a nearby kibbutz, and explained that they had temporarily left their house for a safer part of the Galilee. He knew that disclosing that they had crossed over the border into Lebanon would only stir trouble and might even be grounds for expelling his family. These kibbutzniks liked Hamoud, knowing nothing of his role in the resistance. Hamda hated that Hamoud was friends with them. He was fraternising with the enemy. 'You never know when they might come in handy,' he would say defensively. Sure enough, upon Hamoud's request, the kibbutzniks approached the army commander, asking for permission on behalf of Hamoud and Hamda to set up their beit sha'ar on the land beside the stone house so that they could tend to their crops and animals. Seeing no particular harm in allowing a Bedouin family to live nearby, the commander agreed. Wasting no time, Hamoud and Hamda moved their family to the plot of land next to their house. They were edging slowly closer to their home. But living so close by and seeing the house being used by the Zionist commander and his troops was almost worse than being away from it. Hamda seethed with rage at the thought of these men occupying her home. After all they had been through to come back, she would not allow the people who had driven her friends and family out of their land to live in her own house. She simply had to find a way back inside.

Hamda hatched a new plan. One day, she asked Hamoud to invite his friends from the kibbutz for dinner along with the Zionist commander. Even though he knew that she was up to something, Hamoud did as he was told. The night of the visit was stormy, with relentless rains and howling winds. Yet the beit sha'ar held tight, and the fire inside made for a cosy setting. When the guests arrived, they gasped in awe at the feast that Hamda had prepared, unaccustomed to such hospitality. As they began to eat, Hamda slipped outside unnoticed and untied the ropes that anchored the beit sha'ar to the ground. As she sat back down inside, she caught Hamoud's eye and winked. He cursed under his breath. Before long, a huge gust of wind lifted the roof of the beit sha'ar and, in one sudden swoop, blew it away. The guests panicked as they were plunged into darkness and no longer sheltered from the rains and the wind. Picking up the trays of food, they told their hosts to hurry into the stone house with the children and their belongings. Hamoud and Hamda did as they were told, grabbing what they could and rushing into the main room of their house, where they settled next to the fire. Here they huddled together through the night, while their dinner 'guests' retired to another room. Hamda didn't sleep a wink. At long last, they were back.

After sheltering in the stone house a few days, Hamda displayed no intention of ever returning to the beit sha'ar. Besides, most of it had been damaged in the storm, and there was nowhere for them to go. The commander was soon informed that these were the stone house's original owners, who had merely sought shelter from the fighting a few months earlier. Even had he not been told, this fact would have been clear from the way Hamda swanned about the house. She treated the commander and his soldiers with disdain, making it known that their presence was a nuisance to her. Hamoud followed Hamda's lead and went about life as though nothing had ever happened, though inwardly he was uncomfortable with his wife's behaviour. While she was stubbornly confident, he wanted to tell her that they wouldn't last long, that the Zionists would soon dump them somewhere, as they had done with so many other families. But to his surprise, that didn't happen.

One day, they received word that Dheeba was coming home. Noura's husband had arranged for her to come back with the Red Cross, since Dheeba was considered young enough to merit reunification with her family in Palestine. Soon after this news arrived, the soldiers stationed in the house slowly began to be deployed to other parts of the border. One by one they left, taking their radios, guns and supplies with them. Then, one morning, the commander and the last two soldiers announced that they were also leaving for good. Hamda was sure that Dheeba's imminent return was responsible. Her daughter was her totem against the evil eye.

On the day of the commander's departure, Hamda followed him out the house, shutting the door in his face before he could even say goodbye. She turned to her husband, sumud emanating from every pore of her body, and smiled. Hamoud cracked a faint smile back. He was softening. Hamda knew that deep down, Hamoud held her responsible for their separation from their eldest daughter. She had convinced her husband to allow Dheeba to stay with Noura, and she too had forced them to leave Lebanon and return to Palestine. Hamda had spent many sleepless nights wracked with guilt that she had left their daughter behind on the other side of the Lebanese border. But when the Red Cross car pulled up to the stone house, all remorse and resentment evaporated, and Dheeba's parents rushed out to embrace her.

Dheeba was married a few years later. One of Hamoud's acquaintances, a good-looking young fallah from Tarshiha, had asked for her hand, and she had eagerly accepted. Hamda was sure that behind his solemn demeanour, Kamel al-Hawari was a kind man. She had heard that he had suffered tragic losses during the Catastrophe. His family home was bombed in the final attack on the Galilee, and his first wife and child had been killed. She wondered which of the bombs that they had heard from Lebanon had been the one to fall on his house, and what life would be like for Dheeba in the shadow of a deceased wife. But they had all suffered loss in one way or another. Now was the time to create new life, and she was confident that Kamel would provide her daughter with a good home in which to do so.

On Dheeba's wedding day, Hamda presented her with a bedspread that she had spent hours embroidering. She held her daughter tight and wept. She would miss her presence, but this was how it was supposed to be; Dheeba wanted to start her own family. The wedding was a joyful affair, the first that Hamda had attended since the Catastrophe. She felt her body relax as she watched her daughter dance with her new husband. The atmosphere of laughter was infectious; Hamda hadn't realised how much she had missed the company of others. When she returned home, however, her daughter's absence was acutely felt in the house.

One night in the summer of 1956, the Zionists returned to the stone house. This time, they came as the Israeli army, banging on the doors of the house and screaming in Hebrew. Waking from sleep, Hamoud calmly dressed and opened the door. The soldiers charged in, pushing Hamoud and his eldest son up against the wall with their hands behind their backs. Hamda and the rest of the family were forced into a corner of the house. The children were screaming and crying, but Hamda didn't make a noise. She kept her eyes on her husband and her son as they were arrested and loaded onto a truck at gunpoint, before being driven off into the darkness.

Hamda and the rest of her children were given a short while to gather their possessions. Having bundled as much as they could carry into blankets, they too were forced onto a truck at gunpoint and driven forty kilometres south, where they were dumped on the road near the village of Tamra. Hamda felt humiliated. It was as if they were bags of rubbish to be disposed of at will. But she wouldn't let herself break down. 'Not now, not yet,' she would repeat to herself as she held back her tears.

They sought shelter with a distant relative who lived nearby. As soon as Hamoud and their eldest son were released, the family hired a lawyer and submitted a complaint to the courts. Hamda knew it was pointless to ask the very people who had stolen her house for permission to return to it. As expected, the court merely affirmed their exile. A military order declared their house and land sealed off for security purposes and prohibited them from setting foot there again. They were offered a small plot elsewhere as a form of compensation, which they refused. They would not accept the theft of their ancestral land. Overnight, they had become internally displaced. Muhajireen.

Eventually, after a few weeks, the family decided to move to Tarshiha. Dheeba had already made a life for herself there. Moreover, because the majority of the villagers had been expelled, there were houses that they could rent. And so Hamda and Hamoud followed their eldest daughter to start a new life. Just as in Lebanon, Hamda was adamant that their home in Tarshiha would be temporary. And this time they were muhajireen, not laji'een—they were still inside the state borders—and so their return seemed a lot more likely. She followed cases of other muhajireen, especially those from Iqrit and Kufr Bir'im, with great interest because of the similarity of their situations. If the day came that others were allowed home, she and her family too would surely be permitted to return.

In November 1948, the people of Iqrit and Kufr Bir'im had been told by the Israeli army to leave their homes for two weeks, after which time they would be allowed to come back. In both cases, the soldiers said that the villagers' lives were under threat and that the army would protect their homes, but that it couldn't do so unless they were emptied of their inhabitants. This was a poor excuse, and the villagers knew it. The real reason was that their lands were considered to be of strategic importance, situated on hilltops only a few kilometres south of the Lebanese border. But having no choice, the villagers packed up and left to stay with friends and family in neighbouring communities. Two weeks came and went, and the army still did not let them go home. They would sometimes return in secret to tend to their gardens and feed the chickens, to light candles in the churches and say their prayers. The villagers fought hard to go back, even using the Israeli state's legal system to pursue their case. After a few years, the High Court granted permission for the people of both villages to return to their lands, but the court ruling was overruled by the army. In an act of spite, a year later, the army blew up the remaining houses in both Iqrit and Kufr Bir'im. Two decades since their expulsion, the villagers had still been unable to return home.

A knock at the door startled Hamda, and she turned to the window to see her eldest daughter outside. 'The boys left,' Dheeba said as she entered, kissing her mother on both cheeks. Hamda could see her worries for Mahmoud written all over her face. 'They'll be fine, yimma,' she said reassuringly. And she was certain they would be. It was a school trip, and both boys were responsible. Of all Dheeba's children, Hamda had a soft spot for Mahmoud; he was kind, but also incredibly cheeky, confident and curious. He visited her and Hamoud often and asked them questions about everything. Sometimes, he brought his friends with him, and she would delight them with sweets and treats. Over time, Hamda had become known in the village as Al-Habbaba, the loved one. She pretended not to take notice, but secretly she loved the nickname.

Hamda watched as Dheeba went over to her father and kissed him on the head. He grunted in acknowledgement of her presence. Hamda fetched another glass of tea and placed it on a tray with a tin of biscuits. She gestured for Dheeba to move out into the garden. 'Let's sit outside, it's nice weather,' she said, grabbing the bag of akkoub from the doorstep. They sat down on a wooden bench. Dheeba placed her tattoo-faded hand on her mother's. She was an affectionate woman, showing her love through small physical gestures.

'How was the house?' Dheeba asked. The Zionists had recently celebrated their Independence Day, an event that Hamda cursed over and over. Every year, the whole country was forced to celebrate the holiday, with strict surveillance to see who shirked the festivities. But as vile as this day was, it also presented an opportunity. Since the Catastrophe, the Israeli military regime had placed them under tight control. But when restrictions had been eased a few years ago, they were given permission to move without permits on Israel's Independence Day. It was Hamda's idea to use this rare freedom to go back and see their house. Packing some of the children into a borrowed car, along with a picnic, she would set off for the northern road on the same day every year. The house was less than an hour's drive away. Hamoud had parked the car at the bottom of the dirt track. The children, not listening to their father's warnings to be careful, ran up to the house and climbed over the barbed wire, shouting joyfully. Hamda felt Hamoud's hand on her back, giving her a gentle push towards her home.

Hamda briefly closed her eyes and exhaled slowly. 'It's still there, al-hamdillah,' she told her daughter, who had been waiting patiently for an answer. Hamda handed Dheeba a pair of scissors and a thistly akkoub. Without saying another word, they both began cutting away the spikes.

EPILOGUE

Mahmoud stood facing the stone house. His wife, Helen, and their children, Tariq and Yara, were not far behind. He jumped over the barbed wire as Helen called after him to be careful, a tinge of worry creeping into her expression. The children, meanwhile, paid their father no attention. Yara was dawdling while Tariq looked for something in the bushes, no doubt a big stick to play with. Mahmoud turned back towards the house. Walking along its north-facing wall, he ran his fingers across the stones and made his way to the entrance, which was almost blocked by an unruly carob tree. He emptied a bottle of water at its roots, patting the tree as if it were a thirsty animal, before proceeding inside.

There was a strong stench of urine and animal faeces. The house's walls were etched with graffiti, and there was rubbish everywhere. But there was no structural damage. Mahmoud knocked the wall with his fist, as if to make sure it wouldn't crumble. He turned to the first room on the right. In one of the corners was a chimney, the walls around it still blackened with soot. Faint memories slowly trickled back to him. It was here that they had sat during the winter. He even began to remember the smell of burning wood. Or had he imagined that? That was the funny thing about memory. You could never be sure if it was a product of a fixed moment in time, or if it had evolved and mingled with other pieces of the past.

Mahmoud pivoted towards the west-facing window. In the distance he could make out the glistening Mediterranean Sea and the hazy Carmel mountain range that sat above Haifa. He closed his eyes and took a deep breath.

'Mahmoud?' he heard from outside. 'Come and tell the children why we're here.'

Mahmoud made his way out to where his wife and children stood waiting. By the doorway, he plucked a pod from the carob tree and handed it to his daughter. 'Save this for Al-Habbaba,' he said. Yara twiddled with the pod in her hand, before putting it in her pocket and skipping back towards the car.

ACKNOWLEDGEMENTS

Firstly, thank you to Brekhna and Farhaana, the editors and founders of Hajar Press, who gave me the opportunity to explore this kind of writing, as I have wanted to do for so long.

Thank you to Baba, Mama, Amto Nizar and many others in my family, who have passed on their memories to me and filled my life with stories from my ancestors. Thank you to my partner, who encouraged me to pursue this project and kept me sane in the midst of pandemic despair.

Thank you to all the resistance fighters who continue to struggle even when it seems all is lost, and especially amongst them the Palestinian women who continue to be the brightest lights in my life.

And finally, thank you to Hamda, who, despite being told by a man that it was not possible, returned to Palestine.